Awarded to

Marjorie Postma

Lamar Plat. S.S. Nov. 14/48

CHRISTIAN SERVICE SONGS

Compiled By

HOMER RODEHEAVER • **GEORGE W. SANVILLE**

Y. P. RODEHEAVER • **J. N. RODEHEAVER**

IRVIN H. MACK

—

Music Editors

B. D. ACKLEY *and* **C. AUSTIN MILES**

—

Artistic Waterproof Cloth Binding
Heavy Bristol Paper

ORCHESTRATIONS

1. Violin Obligato or Flute
2. First Violin (or C Melody Saxophone)
3. Second Violin
4. Cello and Bass
5. First B♭ Clarinet
6. Second B♭ Clarinet
7. E♭ Alto Saxophone
8. E♭ Alto Horns
9. Cornets (1st and 2nd)
10. Trombone (Treble)
11. Trombone (Bass)

—

Published by

The RODEHEAVER Co.
HALL-MACK
WINONA LAKE, INDIANA
Printed in U. S. A.
1947

"CHRISTIAN SERVICE SONGS"

PREFACE

It is with a deep and reverent sense of confidence and pride that we present our new book, "CHRISTIAN SERVICE SONGS."

Confidence because we know in our hearts that you will find here a well-balanced collection of the best standard hymns and gospel songs that will meet every church requirement.

Pride in a work well done. True to our ideal of "Up-holding a High Standard" the compilers of "CHRISTIAN SERVICE SONGS" spent several years examining and studying more than 10,000 hymns and songs, making their selection by **testing** and **retesting** in large congregations and on the radio.

We make each song book our 100% best, improving it over previous books through the creation and careful testing of new songs, and careful analysis of what is most useful of the old hymns and gospel songs.

With confidence and pride we present

"CHRISTIAN SERVICE SONGS"—
a real aid to
CHRISTIAN SERVICE in YOUR church.

1

O COULD I SPEAK

Samuel Medley

Dr. Lowell Mason

1. O could I speak the match-less worth, O could I sound the
2. I'd sing the pre-cious blood He spilt, My ran-som from the
3. I'd sing the char-ac-ters He bears, And all the forms of
4. Well, the de-light-ful day will come When my dear Lord will

glo-ries forth Which in my Sav-iour shine, I'd soar, and touch the
dread-ful guilt Of sin, and wrath di-vine: I'd sing His glo-rious
love He wears, Ex-alt-ed on His throne: In loft-iest songs of
bring me home, And I shall see His face; Then with my Sav-iour,

heav'n-ly strings, And vie with Ga-briel while he sings In
right-eous-ness, In which all-per-fect, heav'n-ly dress My
sweet-est praise, I would to ev-er-last-ing days Make
Broth-er, Friend, A blest e-ter-ni-ty I'll spend, Tri-

notes al-most di-vine, In notes al-most di-vine.
soul shall ev-er shine, My soul shall ev-er shine.
all His glo-ries known, Make all His glo-ries known.
um-phant in His grace, Tri-um-phant in His grace. A-MEN.

2 WONDERFUL

A. H. A.   A. H. ACKLEY

1. Won-der-ful birth, to a man-ger He came, Made in the like-ness of
2. Won-der-ful life, full of serv-ice so free, Friend to the poor and the
3. Won-der-ful death, for it meant not de-feat, Cal-va-ry made His great
4. Won-der-ful hope, He is com-ing a-gain, Com-ing as King o'er the

man, to pro-claim God's boundless love for a world sick with sin, Pleading with
need-y was He; Un-fail-ing goodness on all He bestowed, Un-dy-ing
mis-sion com-plete, Wrought our redemption, and when He a-rose, Ban-ished for-
na-tions to reign; Glo-ri-ous prom-ise, His word can-not fail, His righteous

CHORUS

sin-ners to let Him come in.
faith in the vil-est He showed. } Wonder-ful name He bears, Wonder-ful
ev-er the last of our foes.
kingdom at last must pre-vail!

crown He wears, Wonder-ful blessings His triumphs af-ford; Won-der-ful

Cal-va-ry, Wonder-ful grace for me, Wonder-ful love of my Wonder-ful Lord!

3 JESUS IS ALWAYS THERE

B. M. L.

Bertha Mae Lillenas

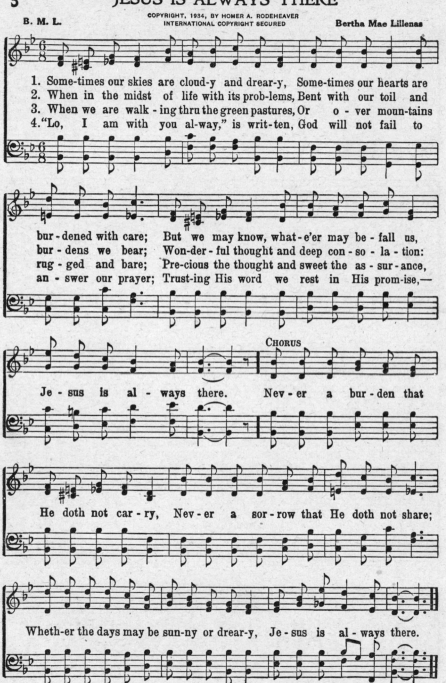

1. Some-times our skies are cloud-y and drear-y, Some-times our hearts are
2. When in the midst of life with its prob-lems, Bent with our toil and
3. When we are walk-ing thru the green pastures, Or o-ver moun-tains
4. "Lo, I am with you al-way," is writ-ten, God will not fail to

bur-dened with care; But we may know, what-e'er may be-fall us,
bur-dens we bear; Won-der-ful thought and deep con-so-la-tion:
rug-ged and bare; Pre-cious the thought and sweet the as-sur-ance,
an-swer our prayer; Trust-ing His word we rest in His prom-ise,—

CHORUS

Je-sus is al-ways there. Nev-er a bur-den that

He doth not car-ry, Nev-er a sor-row that He doth not share;

Wheth-er the days may be sun-ny or drear-y, Je-sus is al-ways there.

4 HALLELUJAH! WHAT A SAVIOUR

P. P. B.

P. P. Bliss

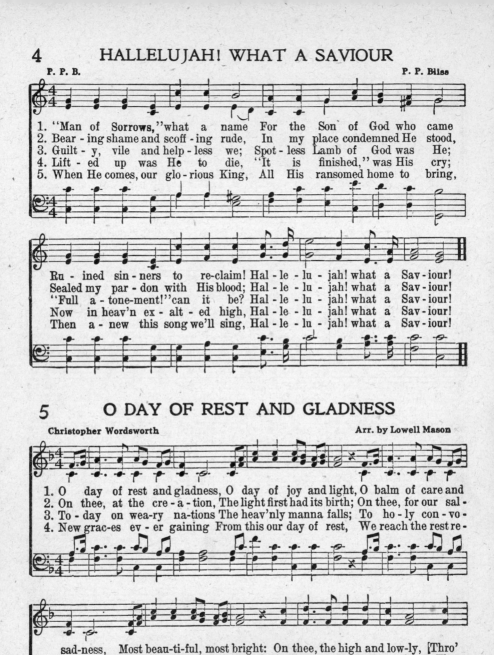

1. "Man of Sorrows," what a name For the Son of God who came
2. Bear-ing shame and scoff-ing rude, In my place condemned He stood,
3. Guilt-y, vile and help-less we; Spot-less Lamb of God was He;
4. Lift-ed up was He to die, "It is finished," was His cry;
5. When He comes, our glo-rious King, All His ransomed home to bring,

Ru-ined sin-ners to re-claim! Hal-le-lu-jah! what a Sav-iour!
Sealed my par-don with His blood; Hal-le-lu-jah! what a Sav-iour!
"Full a-tone-ment!" can it be? Hal-le-lu-jah! what a Sav-iour!
Now in heav'n ex-alt-ed high, Hal-le-lu-jah! what a Sav-iour!
Then a-new this song we'll sing, Hal-le-lu-jah! what a Sav-iour!

5 O DAY OF REST AND GLADNESS

Christopher Wordsworth

Arr. by Lowell Mason

1. O day of rest and gladness, O day of joy and light, O balm of care and
2. On thee, at the cre-a-tion, The light first had its birth; On thee, for our sal-
3. To-day on wea-ry na-tions The heav'nly manna falls; To ho-ly con-vo-
4. New grac-es ev-er gaining From this our day of rest, We reach the rest re-

sad-ness, Most beau-ti-ful, most bright: On thee, the high and low-ly, [Thro'
va-tion, Christ rose from depths of earth; On thee, our Lord, vic-to-rious, The
ca-tions The sil-ver trump-et calls, Where gospel light is glow-ing With
main-ing To spir-its of the blest; To Ho-ly Ghost be prais-es, To

O DAY OF REST AND GLADNESS

a - ges joined in tune, Sing "Ho-ly, ho-ly, ho-ly," To the great God Tri-une.
Spirit sent from heav'n; And thus on Thee, most glorious, A tri - ple light was giv'n.
pure and radiant beams, And liv-ing wa-ter flow-ing With soul-re-fresh-ing streams.
Fa-ther, and to Son; The church her voice upraises To Thee, blest Three in One.

6 WHEN MORNING GILDS THE SKIES

Translated from the German by Edward Caswall

Joseph Barnby

1. When morn-ing gilds the skies, My heart a - wak-ing cries,
2. When-e'er the sweet church bell Peals o - ver hill and dell
3. The night be-comes as day, When from the heart we say,
4. In heav'n's e - ter - nal bliss The love- liest strain is this,
5. Be this, while life is mine, My can - ti - cle di - vine,

May Je - sus Christ be praised! A - like at work and pray'r,
May Je - sus Christ be praised! Oh! hark to what it sings,
May Je - sus Christ be praised! The pow'rs of dark-ness fear,
May Je - sus Christ be praised! Let earth, and sea, and sky,
May Je - sus Christ be praised! Be this th'e-ter - nal song

To Je - sus I re - pair; May Je - sus Christ be praised!
As joy - ous-ly it rings, May Je - sus Christ be praised!
When this sweet chant they hear, May Je - sus Christ be praised!
From depth to height re - ply, May Je - sus Christ be praised!
Through all the a - ges long, May Je - sus Christ be praised! A-men.

7 SOMEBODY CARES

Fannie Edna Stafford

Homer A. Rodeheaver

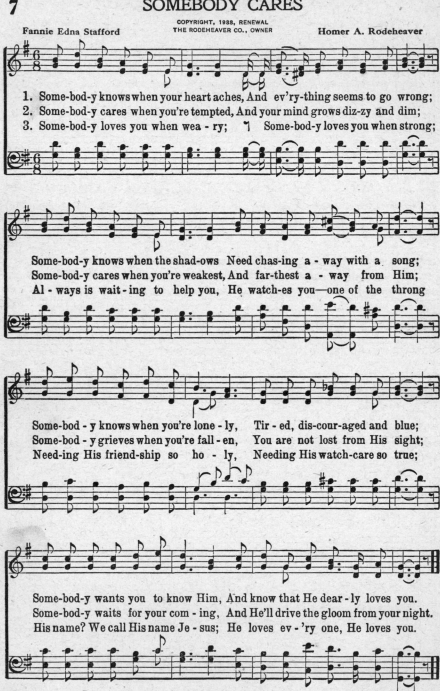

1. Some-bod-y knows when your heart aches, And ev'ry-thing seems to go wrong;
2. Some-bod-y cares when you're tempted, And your mind grows diz-zy and dim;
3. Some-bod-y loves you when wea - ry; ♪ Some-bod-y loves you when strong;

Some-bod-y knows when the shad-ows Need chas-ing a - way with a song;
Some-bod-y cares when you're weakest, And far-thest a - way from Him;
Al - ways is wait-ing to help you, He watch-es you—one of the throng

Some-bod - y knows when you're lone - ly, Tir - ed, dis-cour-aged and blue;
Some-bod - y grieves when you're fall - en, You are not lost from His sight;
Need-ing His friend-ship so ho - ly, Needing His watch-care so true;

Some-bod-y wants you to know Him, And know that He dear - ly loves you.
Some-bod-y waits for your com - ing, And He'll drive the gloom from your night.
His name? We call His name Je - sus; He loves ev - 'ry one, He loves you.

8 BE STILL MY SOUL

KATHARINA VON SCHLEGEL, Tr. by JANE L. BORTHWICK   JEAN SIBELIUS

1. Be still, my soul: the Lord is on thy side; .... Bear pa-tient-
2. Be still, my soul: thy God doth un - der - take .... To guide the
3. Be still, my soul: the hour is has- tening on .... When we shall

ly the cross of grief or pain; Leave to thy God to
fu - ture as He has the past. Thy hope, thy con - fi -
be for ev - er with the Lord, When dis - ap - point - ment,

or - der and pro - vide; ...... In ev - 'ry change He faith - ful will re -
dence let noth -ing shake; ... All now mys - te - rious shall be bright at
grief, and fear are gone, ... Sor-row for - got, love's pur - est joys re -

main...... Be still, my soul: thy best, thy heav'n- ly Friend......
last .... Be still, my soul: the waves and winds still know........
stored..... Be still, my soul: when change and tears are past, ...

Thro' thorn- y ways leads to a joy- ful end......
His voice who ruled them while He dwelt be - low......
All safe and bless - ed we shall meet at last...... A - men.

Music used by permission of the Presbyterian Board of Christian Education, owner of the special arrangement of this tune made in 1932

9 YES, THE LORD CAN DEPEND ON ME

Elsie Duncan Yale

J. Lincoln Hall

1. There are fields that to har-vest are white, And a reap-er with
2. There's a mes-sage to bear far and near, Of a Sav-iour whose
3. There are souls who are drift-ing a-way, Let me bring them, dear

joy I will be; Gold-en sheaves will I bring, to my Mas-ter and King,
love sets us free, And the call ring-ing clear, glad of heart will I hear,
Lord, un-to Thee; I will seek them to-day, I will haste nor de-lay,

CHORUS

For the Lord can de-pend on me! Yes, the Lord can de-pend on

me, Yes, the Lord can de-pend on me; And His name I'll con-
on me, on me;

fess, un-to Him I say "Yes," For the Lord can de-pend on me!

JOHN NEWTON

LOWELL MASON

1. Safe - ly through an - oth - er week God has brought us on our way;
2. While we pray for par-d'ning grace, Thro' the dear Re-deem-er's name,
3. Here we come Thy name to praise, Let us feel Thy pres-ence near;
4. May Thy gos-pel's joy-ful sound Con-quer sin-ners, com-fort saints;

Let us now a bless-ing seek, Wait-ing in His courts to - day;
Show Thy rec - on - cil - ed face; Take a - way our sin and shame:
May Thy glo - ry meet our eyes, While we in Thy house ap - pear:
Make the fruits of grace a - bound, Bring re - lief for all com - plaints:

Day of all the week the best, Em-blem of e - ter - nal rest: Day of
From our world-ly cares set free, May we rest this day in Thee: From our
Here af - ford us, Lord, a taste Of our ev - er-last-ing feast: Here af-
Thus may all our Sab-baths prove, Till we join the Church a - bove: Thus may

all the week the best, Em - blem of e - ter - nal rest.
world-ly cares set free, May we rest this day in Thee.
ford us, Lord, a taste Of our ev - er - last-ing feast.
all our Sab-baths prove, Till we join the Church a - bove. A - MEN.

11 A SHARE IN THE ATONEMENT

C. A. M.   C. AUSTIN MILES

1. At one with God, how rich is my con-di-tion; At peace with Him where
2. Condemned was He, but I received a pard-on. A sin-ner, I. The
3. He bore the cross, but I received a bless-ing. All that I have, or

ev-er I may be. Between us, then, all bar-ri-ers were broken When
sin-less One was He. To ran-som me, the Son of God was willing To
am, or hope to be,—This do I owe, nor can I e'er re-pay Him Who

CHORUS

Je-sus made a-tone-ment on Cal-va-ry.⎫
make a full a-tone-ment, on Cal-va-ry.⎬ I have a share in that a-
made complete a-tone-ment on Cal-va-ry.⎭

tone-ment Which was made on Cal-va-ry. What a treasure is mine,

rit.

This gift so di-vine, That no one can take a-way from me.

12 JESUS IS SO WONDERFUL

C. A. M.

C. Austin Miles

Slow

1. Come, ye heav-y la-den Oft by sor-row tried,
2. Think of all the dan-gers He has brought you thru:
3. In your dark-est mo-ments Give to Him your hand;
4. Are your cross-es heav-y? He bore one, a-lone;

Turn your thoughts to Je-sus, Help-er, Friend and Guide.
He has not for-got-ten But re-mem-bers you.
Tell Him all your heart-aches, He will un-der-stand.
Ev-'ry cross you car-ry He takes as His own.

Chorus

Je-sus is so won-der-ful Words can-not ex-press All His lov-ing sym-pa-thy, All His ten-der-ness... Have you walked up Calv'ry way?

He has trod it, too, But the cross He carried there Is not laid on you.

COME, THOU ALMIGHTY KING

ANONYMOUS

FELICE DE GIARDINI

1. Come, Thou Al - might - y King, Help us Thy name to sing,
2. Come, Thou In - car - nate Word, Gird on Thy might - y sword,
3. Come, Ho - ly Com - fort - er, Thy sa - cred wit - ness bear
4. To the great One in Three E - ter - nal prais - es be

Help us to praise: Fa - ther, all - glo - ri - ous, O'er all vic -
Our pray'r at - tend: Come, and Thy peo - ple bless, And give Thy
In this glad hour: Thou who al - might - y art, Now rule in
Hence ev - er - more. His sov - 'reign maj - es - ty May we in

to - ri - ous, Come, and reign o - ver us, An - cient of Days.
word suc - cess: Spir - it of ho - li - ness, On us de - scend.
ev - 'ry heart, And ne'er from us de - part, Spir - it of pow'r.
glo - ry see, And to e - ter - ni - ty, Love and a - dore.

14 PRAY ON

OSWALD J. SMITH
DUET

CLARENCE KOHLMANN

1. Pray on, O soul of mine, pray on! This night of sin will soon be gone,
2. Pray on, O soul of mine, pray on! Tempta - tions can - not last for long,
3. Pray on, O soul of mine, pray on! The Lord will keep thee true and strong

PRAY ON

The break of day will come ere long Till then, my soul, pray on!........
Thou soon shalt sing the victor's song, With faith, my soul, pray on!........
And an-swer all thy pray'rs ere long With joy my soul, pray on!........

15 HOLY, HOLY, HOLY, LORD GOD ALMIGHTY

Reginald Heber   NICÆA. 11. 12. 11. 12.   John B. Dykes

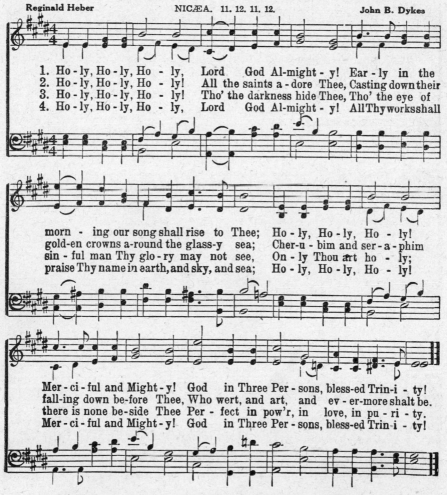

1. Ho - ly, Ho - ly, Ho - ly, Lord God Al-might - y! Ear - ly in the
2. Ho - ly, Ho - ly, Ho - ly! All the saints a - dore Thee, Casting down their
3. Ho - ly, Ho - ly, Ho - ly! Tho' the darkness hide Thee, Tho' the eye of
4. Ho - ly, Ho - ly, Ho - ly, Lord God Al-might - y! All Thy works shall

morn - ing our song shall rise to Thee; Ho - ly, Ho - ly, Ho - ly!
gold-en crowns a-round the glass-y sea; Cher-u - bim and ser - a - phim
sin - ful man Thy glo - ry may not see, On - ly Thou art ho - ly;
praise Thy name in earth, and sky, and sea; Ho - ly, Ho - ly, Ho - ly!

Mer - ci - ful and Might - y! God in Three Per - sons, bless-ed Trin-i - ty!
fall-ing down be-fore Thee, Who wert, and art, and ev - er-more shalt be.
there is none be-side Thee Per - fect in pow'r, in love, in pu - ri - ty.
Mer - ci - ful and Might - y! God in Three Per - sons, bless-ed Trin-i - ty!

PENTECOSTAL POWER

CHARLOTTE G. HOMER   CHAS. H. GABRIEL

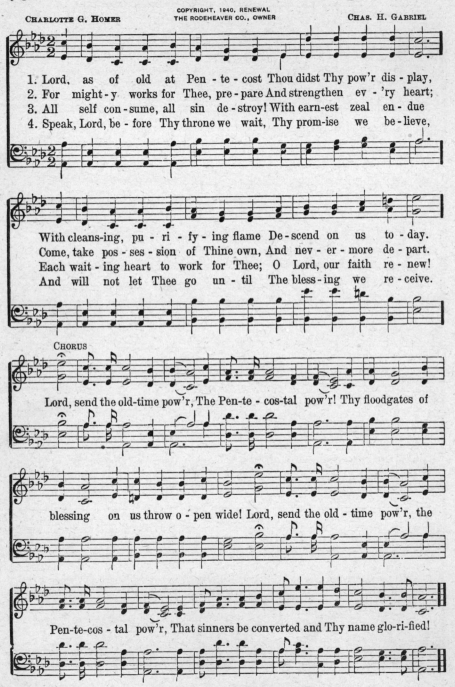

1. Lord, as of old at Pen-te-cost Thou didst Thy pow'r dis-play,
2. For might-y works for Thee, pre-pare And strengthen ev-'ry heart;
3. All self con-sume, all sin de-stroy! With earn-est zeal en-due
4. Speak, Lord, be-fore Thy throne we wait, Thy prom-ise we be-lieve,

With cleans-ing, pu-ri-fy-ing flame De-scend on us to-day.
Come, take pos-ses-sion of Thine own, And nev-er-more de-part.
Each wait-ing heart to work for Thee; O Lord, our faith re-new!
And will not let Thee go un-til The bless-ing we re-ceive.

CHORUS

Lord, send the old-time pow'r, The Pen-te-cos-tal pow'r! Thy floodgates of

blessing on us throw o-pen wide! Lord, send the old-time pow'r, the

Pen-te-cos-tal pow'r, That sinners be converted and Thy name glo-ri-fied!

17 JOY IN SERVING JESUS

Rev. Oswald J. Smith   B. D. Ackley

1. There is joy in serv-ing Je-sus, As I jour-ney on my way,
2. There is joy in serv-ing Je-sus, Joy that tri-umphs o-ver pain;
3. There is joy in serv-ing Je-sus, As I walk a-lone with God;
4. There is joy in serv-ing Je-sus, Joy a-mid the dark-est night,

Joy that fills the heart with prais-es, Ev-'ry hour and ev-'ry day.
Fills my soul with heav-en's mu-sic, Till I join the glad re-frain.
'Tis the joy of Christ, my Sav-iour, Who the path of suf-f'ring trod.
For I've learned the wondrous se-cret, And I'm walk-ing in the light.

CHORUS

There is joy, joy, Joy in serv-ing Je-sus, Joy that throbs with-

in my heart; Ev-'ry mo-ment, ev-'ry hour, As I draw up-

on His pow'r, There is joy, joy, Joy that nev-er shall de-part.

BLEST BE THE TIE

John Fawcett

Hans G. Naegeli

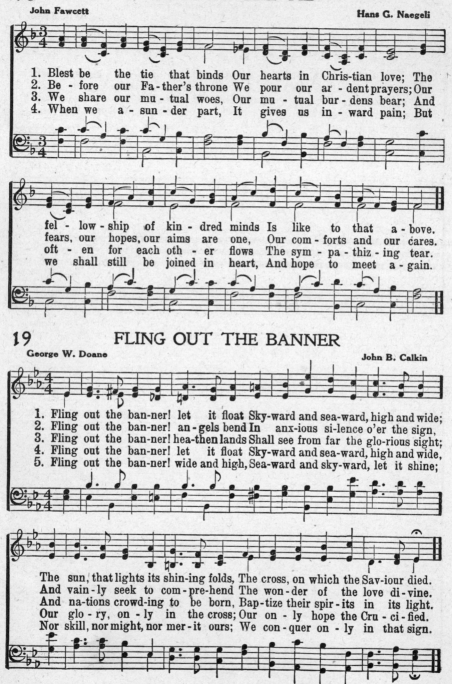

1. Blest be the tie that binds Our hearts in Chris-tian love; The
2. Be - fore our Fa - ther's throne We pour our ar - dent prayers; Our
3. We share our mu - tual woes, Our mu - tual bur - dens bear; And
4. When we a - sun - der part, It gives us in - ward pain; But

fel - low-ship of kin - dred minds Is like to that a - bove.
fears, our hopes, our aims are one, Our com - forts and our cares.
oft - en for each oth - er flows The sym - pa - thiz - ing tear.
we shall still be joined in heart, And hope to meet a - gain.

19   FLING OUT THE BANNER

George W. Doane

John B. Calkin

1. Fling out the ban-ner! let it float Sky-ward and sea-ward, high and wide;
2. Fling out the ban-ner! an - gels bend In anx-ious si-lence o'er the sign,
3. Fling out the ban-ner! hea-then lands Shall see from far the glo-rious sight;
4. Fling out the ban-ner! let it float Sky-ward and sea-ward, high and wide,
5. Fling out the ban-ner! wide and high, Sea-ward and sky-ward, let it shine;

The sun, that lights its shin-ing folds, The cross, on which the Sav-iour died.
And vain - ly seek to com - pre-hend The won - der of the love di - vine.
And na-tions crowd-ing to be born, Bap-tize their spir - its in its light.
Our glo - ry, on - ly in the cross; Our on - ly hope the Cru - ci - fied.
Nor skill, nor might, nor mer - it ours; We con - quer on - ly in that sign.

20 SAVIOUR, BREATHE AN EVENING BLESSING

EVENING PRAYER

James Edmeston

George C. Stebbins

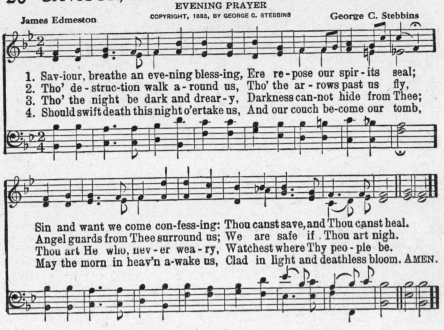

1. Sav-iour, breathe an eve-ning bless-ing, Ere re-pose our spir-its seal;
2. Tho' de-struc-tion walk a-round us, Tho' the ar-rows past us fly,
3. Tho' the night be dark and drear-y, Darkness can-not hide from Thee;
4. Should swift death this night o'ertake us, And our couch be-come our tomb,

Sin and want we come con-fess-ing: Thou canst save, and Thou canst heal.
Angel guards from Thee surround us; We are safe if Thou art nigh.
Thou art He who, nev-er wea-ry, Watchest where Thy peo-ple be.
May the morn in heav'n a-wake us, Clad in light and deathless bloom. AMEN.

21 A CHARGE TO KEEP I HAVE

BOYLSTON S. M.

Charles Wesley

Lowell Mason

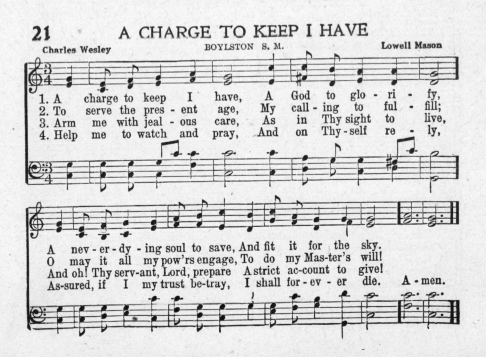

1. A charge to keep I have, A God to glo-ri-fy,
2. To serve the pres-ent age, My call-ing to ful-fill;
3. Arm me with jeal-ous care, As in Thy sight to live,
4. Help me to watch and pray, And on Thy-self re-ly,

A nev-er-dy-ing soul to save, And fit it for the sky.
O may it all my pow'rs engage, To do my Mas-ter's will!
And oh! Thy serv-ant, Lord, prepare A strict ac-count to give!
As-sured, if I my trust be-tray, I shall for-ev-er die. A-men.

22 THE NEED OF THE WORLD IS JESUS

Dedicated to my friend, Arthur W. McKee.—B. D. A.

Oswald J. Smith, D.D.

B. D. Ackley

1. There nev-er was one like the Sav-iour of men, He meets ev-'ry
2. The world does not know Him, this Sav-iour di-vine, And yet He is
3. Your needs may be man-y, your sins may be great, But He is suf-

need of the heart; Then take Him your bur-dens, your sor-rows and cares,
wait-ing to bless; Then go to Him quick-ly and prove Him to-day,
fi-cient for all; He bids you this mo-ment be-lieve and re-joice,

CHORUS

His grace He will glad-ly im-part.
Your need you may free-ly con-fess. The need of the world is
Then trust Him what-ev-er be-fall.

Je-sus, There's no oth-er one who can save— Then why will ye

die, when sal-va-tion is nigh, The need of the world is Je-sus.

ONLY A TOUCH

Ida L. Reed

B. D. Ackley

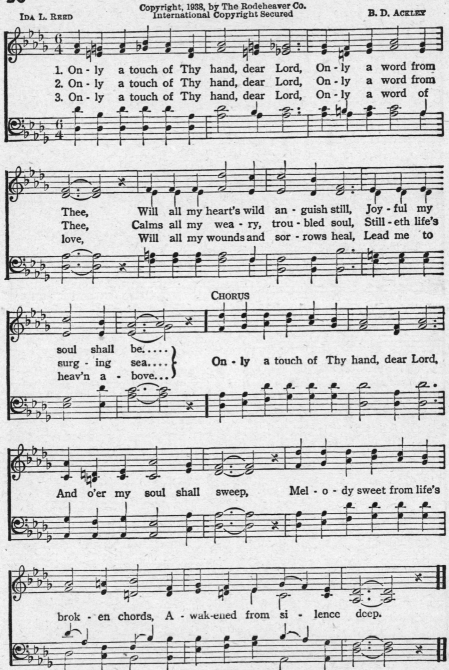

1. On-ly a touch of Thy hand, dear Lord, On-ly a word from Thee, Will all my heart's wild an-guish still, Joy-ful my soul shall be.....
2. On-ly a touch of Thy hand, dear Lord, On-ly a word from Thee, Calms all my wea-ry, trou-bled soul, Still-eth life's surg-ing sea....
3. On-ly a touch of Thy hand, dear Lord, On-ly a word of love, Will all my wounds and sor-rows heal, Lead me to heav'n a-bove...

CHORUS

On-ly a touch of Thy hand, dear Lord, And o'er my soul shall sweep, Mel-o-dy sweet from life's brok-en chords, A-wak-ened from si-lence deep.

24 IN THEE DO I LIVE

C. A. M. C. AUSTIN MILES

1. All that I am or hope to be, O son of God, I owe to Thee,
2. Thy blessed cross has sealed my peace, Thy sorrows make my own to cease;
3. Thy cruel wounds my own have healed; Thy broken heart my par-don sealed;

For Thou has bought me; I am Thine, And by Thy mer-cy Thou art mine.
Thy pow'r has cleansed me from all sin, Thy presence keeps my conscience clean.
Thy death, O Christ, means life for me, A life for all e-ter-ni-ty.

CHORUS

Thy mer-cy sought me, Thy love has bought me, Thy grace has taught me to be-lieve. Then, in be-liev-ing, Thy peace re-ceiv-ing, Now in Thee on-ly, do I live....

25 TRUE-HEARTED, WHOLE-HEARTED

Frances R. Havergal   George C. Stebbins

1. True-hearted, whole-hearted, faith-ful and loy-al, King of our lives, by Thy grace we will be; Un-der the stan-dard ex-alt-ed and roy-al, Strong in Thy strength we will bat-tle for Thee.

2. True-hearted, whole-hearted, full-est al-le-giance, Yielding henceforth to our glo-ri-ous King; Val-iant en-deav-or and lov-ing o-be-dience Free-ly and joy-ous-ly now we would bring.

3. True-hearted, whole-hearted, Sav-ior all-glo-rious! Take Thy great pow-er and reign there a-lone, O-ver our wills and af-fec-tions vic-to-rious, Free-ly sur-ren-dered and whol-ly Thine own.

CHORUS

Peal out the watchword! si-lence it nev-er, Song of our spir-its re-joic-ing and free; Peal out the watch-word! loy-al for-ev-er, King of our lives, by Thy grace we will be.

DAY IS DYING IN THE WEST

MARY A. LATHBURY

WILLIAM F. SHERWIN

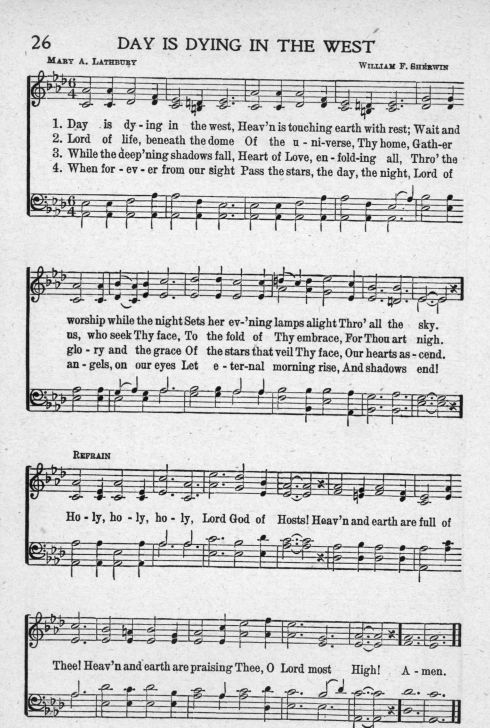

1. Day is dy-ing in the west, Heav'n is touching earth with rest; Wait and
2. Lord of life, beneath the dome Of the u-ni-verse, Thy home, Gath-er
3. While the deep'ning shadows fall, Heart of Love, en-fold-ing all, Thro' the
4. When for-ev-er from our sight Pass the stars, the day, the night, Lord of

worship while the night Sets her ev-'ning lamps alight Thro' all the sky.
us, who seek Thy face, To the fold of Thy embrace, For Thou art nigh.
glo-ry and the grace Of the stars that veil Thy face, Our hearts as-cend.
an-gels, on our eyes Let e-ter-nal morning rise, And shadows end!

REFRAIN

Ho-ly, ho-ly, ho-ly, Lord God of Hosts! Heav'n and earth are full of

Thee! Heav'n and earth are praising Thee, O Lord most High! A-men.

THE CHURCH'S ONE FOUNDATION

SAMUEL J. STONE

SAMUEL S. WESLEY

1. The Church-'s one foun - da - tion Is Je - sus Christ her Lord;
2. E - lect from ev - 'ry na - tion, Yet one o'er all the earth,
3. 'Mid toil and trib - u - la - tion, And tu - mult of her war,
4. Yet she on earth hath un - ion With God the Three in One,

She is His new cre - a - tion By wa - ter and the word:
Her char - ter of sal - va - tion, One Lord, one faith, one birth;
She waits the con - sum - ma - tion Of peace for ev - er - more;
And mys - tic sweet com - mun - ion With those whose rest is won:

From heav'n He came and sought her To be His ho - ly bride; With
One ho - ly name she bless - es, Par - takes one ho - ly food, And
Till, with the vis - ion glo - rious, Her long - ing eyes are blest, And
O hap - py ones and ho - ly! Lord, give us grace that we, Like

His own blood He bought her, And for her life He died.
to one hope she press - es, With ev - 'ry grace en - dued.
the great church vic - to - rious Shall be the church at rest.
them, tho meek and low - ly, On high may dwell with Thee. A - men.

SINCE GOD LOVES ME

A. H. A.

Rev. A. H. Ackley

1. I stand at the dawn of a beau-ti-ful day, Sweet peace fills my
2. The win-ter of sor-row is changed in-to spring, The tears and the
3. The hop-ing and dream-ing have come to an end, The long, wea-ry

heart from a-bove, The fears and misgivings have vanished a-way, Dis-
heartaches are past, The glo-ry of summer now reigns like a king, And
jour-ney is o'er, The new road I trav-el with God as my friend, Leads

CHORUS

pelled by the light of God's love. ⎫ Since God loves me,........ The world is re-
hap-piness greets me at last. ⎬
on to the heav-en-ly door. ⎭ God loves me,

splendent with glad-ness, My soul is free,...... No lon-ger I wan-der in
is free,

sad-ness, Since God loves me,........ To turn from His love would be madness,
God loves me,

SINCE GOD LOVES ME

The joy of the morn-ing, my life is a-dorn-ing, Since God loves me.

29 TILL I BECOME LIKE THEE

Copyright, 1937, by The Rodeheaver Co.

Rev. Edgar H. Peterson   International Copyright Secured   Geo. C. Stebbins

1. O Je - sus, Sav - iour and my Lord, Who liv - est now in me,
2. My way in life which Thou shalt choose, I know will be the best;
3. Tho' oft I can - not un - der - stand The way Thou lead - est me;
4. When in Thine im - age I shall stand, Transformed to be like Thee;

Have Thou Thy way in all my life Till I be - come like Thee.
And thro' the trust I have in Thee, My heart will find its rest.
I ques - tion not Thy way, O Lord, But leave it all to Thee.
What will it be with Thee to dwell Thro' all e - ter - ni - ty?

CHORUS

Like Thee,........ like Thee,........ Till I be - come like Thee;........
Like Thee,   like Thee,   like Thee;

Have Thou Thy way in all my life, Till I be - come like Thee.

ATONEMENT WAS MADE

C. Austin Miles

C. Austin Miles

1. The sto-ry of re-demp-tion still is told (still is told), And it is
2. I looked up-on the cross of Cal-va-ry (Cal-va-ry) One hap-py
3. Of earth be-neath, nor yet of heav'n a-bove (heav'n a-bove), Shall I ask

true (And it is true), it must be true (it must be true); Thru end-less years it
day (One hap-py day), O glo-rious day (O glo-rious day)! And when I felt its
more (Shall I ask more)? no, nothing more (no, nothing more), If I but have the

nev-er shall grow old (ne'er grow old), For-ev-er, it is new (it is new).
pow'r ap-plied to me (un-to me) My bur-dens rolled a-way (rolled a-way).
full-ness of the love (of the love) Of Him whom I a-dore (I a-dore).

CHORUS

It nev-er can grow old, This sto-ry that is told, Of Je-sus and sal-

va-tion full and free (full and free). Tho' king-doms wax and wane, This

ATONEMENT WAS MADE

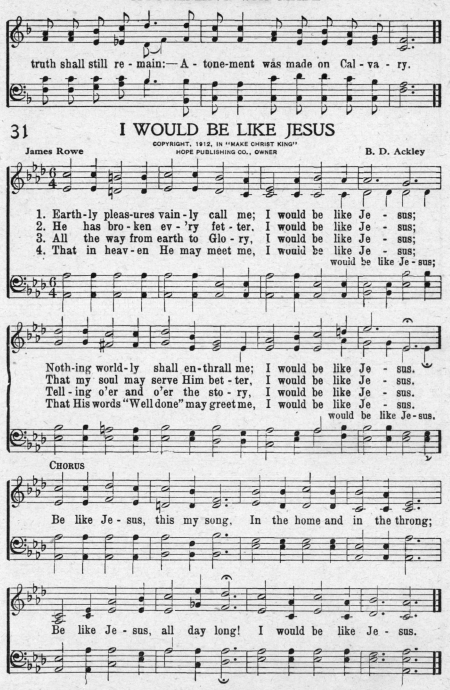

truth shall still re - main:—A - tone-ment was made on Cal - va - ry.

31   I WOULD BE LIKE JESUS

COPYRIGHT, 1912, IN "MAKE CHRIST KING"
HOPE PUBLISHING CO., OWNER

James Rowe   B. D. Ackley

1. Earth-ly pleas-ures vain-ly call me; I would be like Je - sus;
2. He has bro-ken ev-'ry fet-ter. I would be like Je - sus;
3. All the way from earth to Glo-ry, I would be like Je - sus;
4. That in heav-en He may meet me, I would be like Je - sus;

would be like Je - sus;

Noth-ing world-ly shall en-thrall me; I would be like Je - sus.
That my soul may serve Him bet-ter, I would be like Je - sus.
Tell-ing o'er and o'er the sto-ry, I would be like Je - sus.
That His words "Well done" may greet me, I would be like Je - sus.

would be like Je-sus.

CHORUS

Be like Je-sus, this my song, In the home and in the throng;

Be like Je-sus, all day long! I would be like Je - sus.

ABIDE WITH ME

H. F. Lyte

W. H. Monk

1. A - bide with me: fast falls the e - ven - tide; The dark - ness
2. Swift to its close ebbs out life's lit - tle day; Earth's joys grow
3. I need Thy pres - ence ev - 'ry pass - ing hour: What but Thy
4. Hold Thou Thy cross be - fore my clos - ing eyes, Shine thro' the

deep - -ens; Lord, with me a - bide: When oth - er help - ers fail, and
dim, its glo - ries pass a - way; Change and de - cay in all a -
grace can foil the tempt - er's pow'r? Who like Thy - self my guide and
gloom, and point me to the skies: Heav'n's morning breaks, and earth's vain

com - forts flee, Help of the help - less, O a - bide with me!
round I see: O Thou who chang - est not, a - bide with me!
stay can be? Through cloud and sun - shine, O a - bide with me!
shad - ows flee— In life, in death, O Lord, a - bide with me!

33 COME, YE DISCONSOLATE

Thomas Moore, Thomas Hastings

Samuel Webbe

1. Come, ye dis - con - so - late, wher-e'er ye lan - guish; Come to the
2. Joy of the des - o - late, light of the stray - ing, Hope of the
3. Here see the bread of life; see wa - ters flow - ing Forth from the

COME, YE DISCONSOLATE

mer - cy - seat, fer - vent - ly kneel; Here bring your wound-ed hearts,
pen - i - tent, fade - less and pure, Here speaks the Com - fort - er,
throne of God, pure from a - bove; Come to the feast of love;

here tell your an - guish; Earth has no sor-row that Heav'n can-not heal.
ten - der - ly say - ing, "Earth has no sor-row that Heav'n can-not cure."
come, ev - er know-ing Earth has no sor-row but Heav'n can re - move.

SUN OF MY SOUL

34

JOHN KEBLE

PETER RITTER

1. Sun of my soul! Thou Sav-ior dear, It is not night if Thou be near;
2. When the soft dews of kind-ly sleep My wea-ry eye-lids gen-tly steep,
3. A - bide with me from morn till eve, For with-out Thee I can-not live;
4. Be near to bless me when I wake, Ere thro' the world my way I take;

Oh, may no earth-born cloud a - rise To hide Thee from Thy servant's eyes!
Be my last tho't—how sweet to rest For-ev - er on my Sav-iour's breast!
A - bide with me when night is nigh, For without Thee I dare not die.
A - bide with me till in Thy love I lose my - self in heav'n a-bove.

THE WHOLE WIDE WORLD

Rev. J. Demster Hammond — Wm. J. Kirkpatrick

1. The whole wide world for Je-sus, This shall our watchword be, Up-on the highest mountain, Down by the wid-est sea. The whole wide world for Je-sus, To Him all men shall bow, In cit-y or on prai-rie, The world for Je-sus now.

2. The whole wide world for Je-sus, In-spires us with the tho't That ev-'ry son of Ad-am Hath by the blood been bought. The whole wide world for Je-sus, O faint not by the way! The cross shall surely conquer, In this our glo-rious day.

3. The whole wide world for Je-sus, The marching or-der sound, Go ye and preach the gos-pel Wher-ev-er man is found. The whole wide world for Je-sus, Our ban-ner is un-furled, We bat-tle now for Je-sus, And faith demands the world.

4. The whole wide world for Je-sus, In th' Father's home a-bove Are man-y won-drous mansions, Man-sions of light and love. The whole wide world for Je-sus, Ride forth, O conqu'ring King, Thru all the mighty na-tions, The world to glo-ry bring.

CHORUS

The whole wide world, the whole wide world, Pro-claim the gos-pel ti-dings thru the whole wide world; Lift up the cross for Je-sus, His

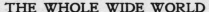

ban-ner be un-furled, Till ev-'ry tongue con-fess Him thru the whole wide world.

36 SOME DAY HE'LL MAKE IT PLAIN

Lida Shivers Leech
COPYRIGHT, 1939, RENEWAL IN "GOSPEL MESSAGE"
INTERNATIONAL COYPRIGHT SECURED
THE RODEHEAVER CO., OWNER
Adam Geibel

Solo, or all in unison

1. I do not know why oft 'round me My hopes all shattered seem to be;
2. I can-not tell the depth of love, Which moves the Father's heart a-bove;
3. Tho' tri-als come thro' passing days, My life will still be filled with praise;

God's perfect plan I can-not see, . . . But some day I'll un-der-stand.
My faith to test, my love to prove, . . . But some day I'll un-der-stand.
For God will lead thro' darkened ways , . . But some day I'll un-der-stand.

CHORUS.

Some day He'll make it plain to me, Some day when I His face shall see;

Some day from tears I shall be free, For some day I shall un - der - stand.

THERE'S A NEW DAY DAWNING

Rev. A. H. Ackley   B. D. Ackley

1. Go forth to serve, as Je - sus went, To min - is - ter to men;
2. Be loy - al to God's Ho - ly Word, De - liv - ered to the saints;
3. Seek Christ, His will, His sac - ri - fice, His bless - ed way to live;

A mes - sen - ger from heav - en sent, To do His work a - gain.
Hold fast the truth that you have heard A-gainst the world's com-plaints.
Let self die out, Christ shall suf - fice, To Him your spir - it give.

CHORUS

There's a new day dawn-ing, There's a new day dawn-ing, Then a - rise, O

chil-dren of the light, A-rise and sing! There's a new day dawn-ing, There's a

new day dawn-ing, When the nations of the world shall worship Christ the King.

38 THE BROKEN THREADS OF LIFE

Oswald J. Smith

B. D. Ackley

Solo

1. Take up the bro-ken threads of life, Thy God can weave the strands a-
2. Take up the bro-ken threads of life; The lost i - deals of oth - er
3. Take up the bro-ken threads of life; The flow'rs that withered long a-

gain; He will not cast His work a - side, Nor suf - fer
days Will be re - born a - mid thy tears, And all thy
go Will bloom a - gain in God's own time, And thou wilt

thee to live in vain. . . Nor suf - fer
heart be filled with praise. . Take up the bro-ken threads of
say, 'twas bet - ter so. . . .

Refrain

life, ... Let God re-store the wasted years; . . . Be - gin this

day to live a - new, ... And bid fare-well, fare-well to all thy fears.

39

NOW THE DAY IS OVER

Sabine Baring-Gould   MERRIAL 6. 5. 6. 5.   Joseph Barnby

1. Now the day is o - ver, Night is draw - ing nigh,
2. Je - sus, give the wea - ry Calm and sweet re - pose;
3. Grant to lit - tle chil - dren Vi - sions bright of Thee;
4. Thro' the long night-watch - es, May Thine an - gels spread
5. When the morn-ing wak - ens, Then may I a - rise,

Shad - ows of the ev - 'ning Steal a - cross the sky.
With Thy ten - d'rest bless - ing May our eye - lids close.
Guard the sail - ors toss - ing On the deep blue sea.
Their white wings a - bove me, Watch - ing 'round my bed.
Pure and fresh and sin - less In Thy ho - ly eyes. A - men.

ev - 'ning Steal a - cross the sky.

40

SOFTLY NOW THE LIGHT OF DAY

George W. Doane   SEYMOUR 7. 7. 7. 7.   Arr. from Carl M. von Weber

1. Soft - ly now the light of day Fades up - on my sight a - way;
2. Thou, whose all - per - vad - ing eye Naught es-capes, with-out, with - in,
3. Soon for me the light of day Shall for ev - er pass a - way;
4. Thou who, sin - less, yet hast known All of man's in - firm - i - ty;

Free from care, from la - bor free, Lord, I would commune with Thee.
Par - don each in - firm - i - ty, O - pen fault, and se-cret sin.
Then, from sin and sor - row free, Take me, Lord, to dwell with Thee.
Then, from Thine e - ter - nal throne, Je - sus, look with pit-ying eye. A - men.

O FOR A THOUSAND TONGUES

AZMON

CHARLES WESLEY

CARL G. GLASER
Arr. by LOWELL MASON

1. O for a thou-sand tongues to sing My great Re-deem-er's praise,
2. My gracious Mas-ter and my God, As-sist me to pro-claim,
3. Je - sus! the name that charms our fears, That bids our sor-rows cease;
4. He breaks the pow'r of canceled sin, He sets the pris-'ner free;
5. Hear Him, ye deaf; His praise, ye dumb, Your loosened tongues em-ploy;

The glo-ries of my God and King, The triumphs of His grace.
To spread thro' all the earth a-broad The hon-ors of Thy name.
'Tis mu-sic in the sin-ner's ears, 'Tis life, and health, and peace.
His blood can make the foul-est clean; His blood a-vailed for me.
Ye blind, be-hold your Sav-ior come; And leap, ye lame, for joy.

42   DEAR LORD AND FATHER OF MANKIND

John G. Whittier

ELTON 8. 6. 8. 8. 6.

Frederick C. Maker

1. Dear Lord and Father of mankind, Forgive our fev'rish ways! Reclothe us in our
2. In simple trust, like theirs who heard, Beside the Syrian sea, The gracious calling
3. O Sabbath rest by Gal - i - lee! O calm of hills a-bove, Where Jesus knelt to
4. Drop Thy still dews of qui-et-ness, Till all our strivings cease; Take from our souls the
5. Breathe thro' the heats of our desire Thy coolness and Thy balm; Let sense be dumb, let

rightful mind; In pur-er lives Thy serv-ice find, In deeper rev'rence, praise.
of the Lord, Let us, like them, without a word, Rise up and fol-low Thee.
share with Thee The silence of e - ter - ni - ty, In - ter-pret-ed by love!
strain and stress, And let our ordered lives confess The beauty of Thy peace.
flesh retire: Speak thro' the earthquake, wind and fire, O still small voice of calm! A-men.

43   HIS GRACE IS SUFFICIENT FOR THEE

S. L.

Scott Lawrence

1, If you would do something for Je-sus, For you He gave all on the
2. If you would be true to your Sav-iour. A loy-al soul win-ner to
3. If you would show others the path-way, Where they can the vic-to-ry

tree, He'll give strength to you, If you're faithful, and true—His grace is suf-
be; Let all the world know. That wher-ev-er you go, His grace is suf-
see, There's no bet-ter way Than by prov-ing each day, His grace is suf-

Chorus

fi-cient for thee, His grace, His mar-vel-ous, won-der-ful

grace is suf-fi-cient for thee; .... His grace, re-
suf-fi-cient for thee;

deem-ing, transforming, sus-tain-ing, a-bund-ant and free! ....
a-bund-ant and free!

44 IN THE SERVICE OF THE KING

A. H. Ackley

B. D. Ackley

1. I am hap-py in the serv-ice of the King, I am hap-py
2. I am hap-py in the serv-ice of the King, I am hap-py
3. I am hap-py in the serv-ice of the King, I am hap-py
4. I am hap-py in the serv-ice of the King, I am hap-py

Oh, so hap-py; I have peace and joy that noth-ing else can bring,
Oh, so hap-py; Thro' the sun-shine and the shad-ow I can sing,
Oh, so hap-py; To His guid-ing hand for-ev-er I will cling,
Oh, so hap-py; All that I pos-sess to Him I glad-ly bring,

REFRAIN.

In the serv-ice of the King. In the serv-ice

of the King Ev-'ry tal-ent I will bring; I have

peace and joy and bless-ing In the serv-ice of the King.

JESUS AND I

C. Austin Miles   M. Isabelle Ritter

1. Walk-ing   in   the morn-ing bright, Glad hours go by,
2. Noon-time!   He   is with me still, The sun rides high;
3. Twi-light   and the shad-ows come, Stars fill the sky;

We two   live in heav'n-ly light— Je-sus and I.
We two   do the Fa-ther's will, Je-sus and I.
We two   safe shall reach our home, Je-sus and I.

REFRAIN

His love has won my heart, He heard my cry,   O may we nev-er part,

Je-sus and I;   He took my sin a-way, He came with

me to stay, Hap-py, I go my way, Con-tent that He is nigh.

NOTE:—Refrain may be used as a Duet by omitting small notes, or Tenor and Soprano may sing these while Alto and Bass sing melody (middle notes).

TELL IT TO-DAY

C. H. G., Jr.

Chas. H. Gabriel, Jr.

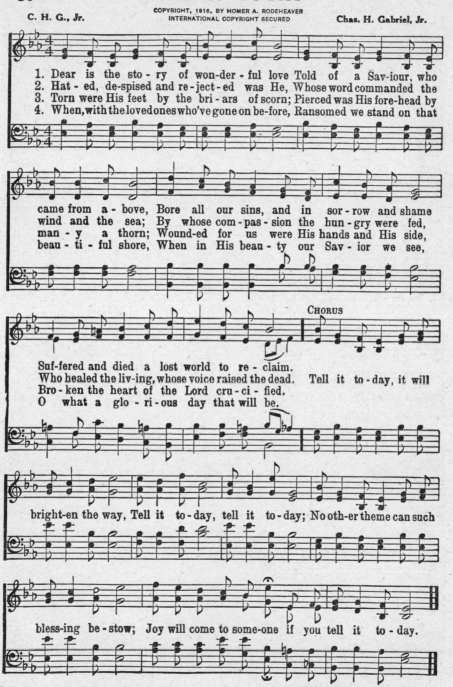

1. Dear is the sto-ry of won-der-ful love Told of a Sav-iour, who
2. Hat-ed, de-spised and re-ject-ed was He, Whose word commanded the
3. Torn were His feet by the bri-ars of scorn; Pierced was His fore-head by
4. When, with the loved ones who've gone on be-fore, Ransomed we stand on that

came from a-bove, Bore all our sins, and in sor-row and shame
wind and the sea; By whose com-pas-sion the hun-gry were fed,
man-y a thorn; Wound-ed for us were His hands and His side,
beau-ti-ful shore, When in His beau-ty our Sav-ior we see,

CHORUS

Suf-fered and died a lost world to re-claim.
Who healed the liv-ing, whose voice raised the dead. Tell it to-day, it will
Bro-ken the heart of the Lord cru-ci-fied.
O what a glo-ri-ous day that will be.

bright-en the way, Tell it to-day, tell it to-day; No oth-er theme can such

bless-ing be-stow; Joy will come to some-one if you tell it to-day.

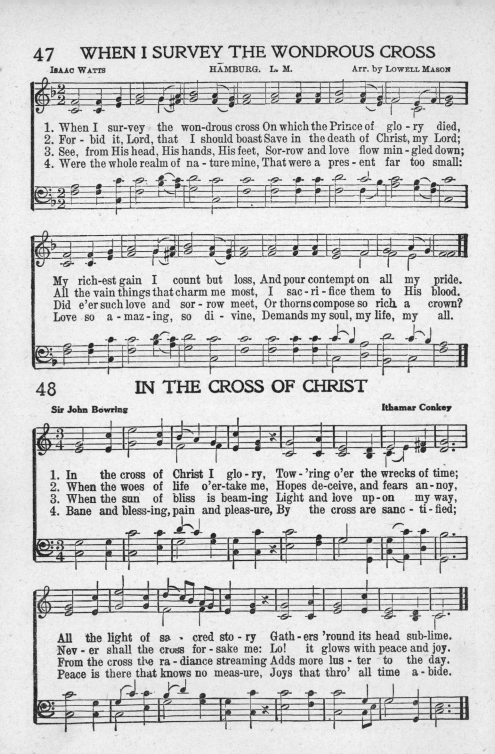

47 WHEN I SURVEY THE WONDROUS CROSS

Isaac Watts   HAMBURG. L. M.   Arr. by Lowell Mason

1. When I sur-vey the won-drous cross On which the Prince of glo - ry died,
2. For - bid it, Lord, that I should boast Save in the death of Christ, my Lord;
3. See, from His head, His hands, His feet, Sor-row and love flow min - gled down;
4. Were the whole realm of na - ture mine, That were a pres - ent far too small:

My rich-est gain I count but loss, And pour contempt on all my pride.
All the vain things that charm me most, I sac - ri - fice them to His blood.
Did e'er such love and sor - row meet, Or thorns compose so rich a crown?
Love so a - maz - ing, so di - vine, Demands my soul, my life, my all.

48 IN THE CROSS OF CHRIST

Sir John Bowring   Ithamar Conkey

1. In the cross of Christ I glo - ry, Tow - 'ring o'er the wrecks of time;
2. When the woes of life o'er-take me, Hopes de-ceive, and fears an - noy,
3. When the sun of bliss is beam-ing Light and love up - on my way,
4. Bane and bless-ing, pain and pleas-ure, By the cross are sanc - ti - fied;

All the light of sa - cred sto - ry Gath-ers 'round its head sub-lime.
Nev - er shall the cross for - sake me: Lo! it glows with peace and joy.
From the cross the ra - diance streaming Adds more lus - ter to the day.
Peace is there that knows no meas-ure, Joys that thro' all time a - bide.

49 COME, HOLY SPIRIT, HEAVENLY DOVE

AZMON. C. M.

Rev. Isaac Watts

Carl G. Gläser
Arr. by Lowell Mason

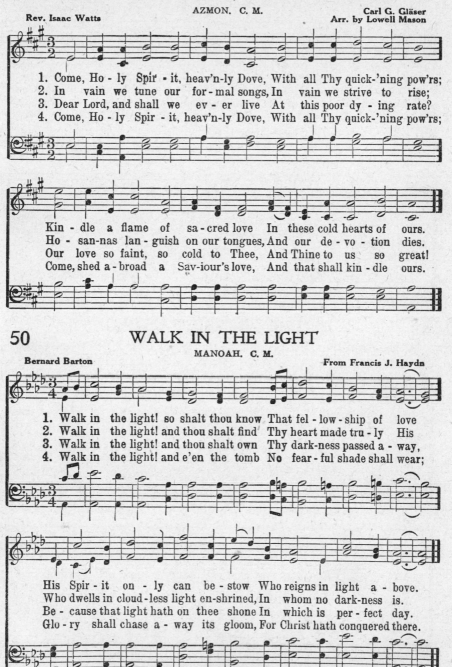

1. Come, Ho - ly Spir - it, heav'n-ly Dove, With all Thy quick-'ning pow'rs;
2. In vain we tune our for-mal songs, In vain we strive to rise;
3. Dear Lord, and shall we ev - er live At this poor dy - ing rate?
4. Come, Ho - ly Spir - it, heav'n-ly Dove, With all Thy quick-'ning pow'rs;

Kin - dle a flame of sa - cred love In these cold hearts of ours.
Ho - san-nas lan - guish on our tongues, And our de - vo - tion dies.
Our love so faint, so cold to Thee, And Thine to us so great!
Come, shed a-broad a Sav-iour's love, And that shall kin - dle ours.

50 WALK IN THE LIGHT

MANOAH. C. M.

Bernard Barton

From Francis J. Haydn

1. Walk in the light! so shalt thou know That fel - low - ship of love
2. Walk in the light! and thou shalt find Thy heart made tru - ly His
3. Walk in the light! and thou shalt own Thy dark-ness passed a - way,
4. Walk in the light! and e'en the tomb No fear - ful shade shall wear;

His Spir - it on - ly can be - stow Who reigns in light a - bove.
Who dwells in cloud-less light en-shrined, In whom no dark-ness is.
Be - cause that light hath on thee shone In which is per - fect day.
Glo - ry shall chase a - way its gloom, For Christ hath conquered there.

51   LET THE CHURCH MARCH ON

A. H. A.

COPYRIGHT, 1939, BY THE RODEHEAVER CO.
INTERNATIONAL COPYRIGHT SECURED.

Rev. A. H. Ackley

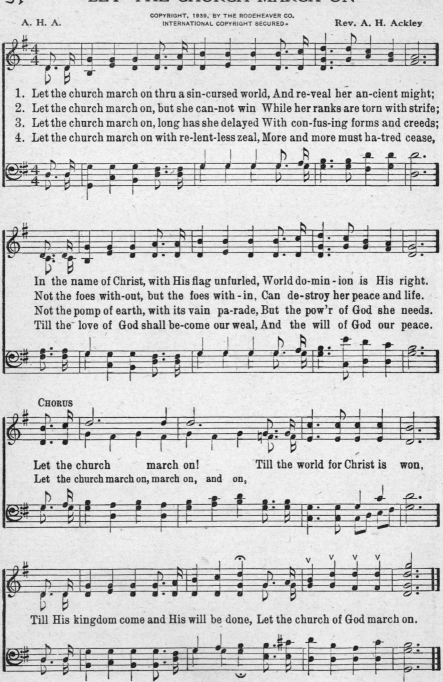

1. Let the church march on thru a sin-cursed world, And re-veal her an-cient might;
2. Let the church march on, but she can-not win While her ranks are torn with strife;
3. Let the church march on, long has she delayed With con-fus-ing forms and creeds;
4. Let the church march on with re-lent-less zeal, More and more must ha-tred cease,

In the name of Christ, with His flag unfurled, World do-min-ion is His right.
Not the foes with-out, but the foes with-in, Can de-stroy her peace and life.
Not the pomp of earth, with its vain pa-rade, But the pow'r of God she needs.
Till the love of God shall be-come our weal, And the will of God our peace.

CHORUS

Let the church   march on!   Till the world for Christ is won,
Let the church march on, march on, and on,

Till His kingdom come and His will be done, Let the church of God march on.

HE KEEPS ON LOVING US STILL

Herbert Buffum

Haldor Lillenas

1. Though far you may wan-der a - way from the fold, Re - fus-ing to
2. His love is far great - er than mor-tals have known, His mer - cy the
3. Though fa - ther or moth - er for - sake us, we know This lov - er of
4. Should we for - sake Him and our love be - come cold, No lon - ger our

yield to His will, This thought is so pre - cious, al-though it be old:
whole earth doth fill; To those who de - ny Him what pa-tience is shown!
souls nev - er will; He fol - lows our foot-steps, wher-e'er they may go,
hearts feel the thrill That once we en - joyed when we en-tered His fold,

CHORUS

"He keeps on lov - ing us still."
He keeps on lov - ing us still.   He keeps on lov - ing us
And keeps on lov - ing us still.
He will keep on lov - ing us still.

still, ... He keeps on lov - ing us still. . . . . Come
lov - ing us still,   lov - ing us still.

loss or come gain, Thru sun-shine or rain, He keeps on lov - ing us still.

NEAR TO THE HEART OF GOD

C. B. McAfee

1. There is a place of qui-et rest, Near to the heart of God,
2. There is a place of com-fort sweet, Near to the heart of God,
3. There is a place of full re-lease, Near to the heart of God,

A place where sin can-not mo-lest, Near to the heart of God.
A place where we our Sav-iour meet, Near to the heart of God.
A place where all is joy and peace, Near to the heart of God.

REFRAIN

O Je-sus, blest Re-deem-er, Sent from the heart of God,

Hold us, who wait be-fore Thee, Near to the heart of God.

54 THERE'S A WIDENESS IN GOD'S MERCY

Rev. F. W. Faber

Lizzie S. Tourjee

1. There's a wide-ness in God's mer-cy Like the wide-ness of the sea;
2. There is wel-come for the sin-ner, And more grac-es for the good;
3. For the love of God is broad-er Than the meas-ure of man's mind,
4. If our love were but more sim-ple, We should take Him at His word;

THERE'S A WIDENESS IN GOD'S MERRCY

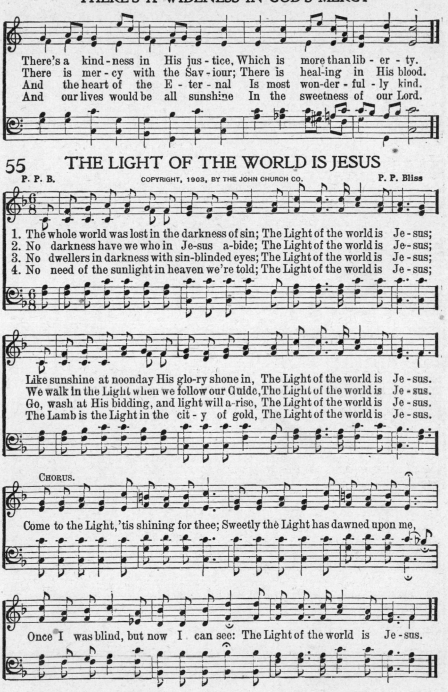

There's a kind-ness in His jus-tice, Which is more than lib - er - ty.
There is mer - cy with the Sav-iour; There is heal-ing in His blood.
And the heart of the E - ter - nal Is most won-der - ful - ly kind.
And our lives would be all sunshine In the sweetness of our Lord.

55   THE LIGHT OF THE WORLD IS JESUS

P. P. B.

P. P. Bliss

1. The whole world was lost in the darkness of sin; The Light of the world is Je - sus;
2. No darkness have we who in Je-sus a-bide; The Light of the world is Je - sus;
3. No dwellers in darkness with sin-blinded eyes; The Light of the world is Je - sus;
4. No need of the sunlight in heaven we're told; The Light of the world is Je - sus;

Like sunshine at noonday His glo-ry shone in, The Light of the world is Je - sus.
We walk in the Light when we follow our Guide, The Light of the world is Je - sus.
Go, wash at His bidding, and light will a-rise, The Light of the world is Je - sus.
The Lamb is the Light in the cit - y of gold, The Light of the world is Je - sus.

CHORUS.

Come to the Light, 'tis shining for thee; Sweetly the Light has dawned upon me,

Once I was blind, but now I can see: The Light of the world is Je - sus.

JESUS, I MY CROSS HAVE TAKEN

HENRY F. LYTE

From MOZART

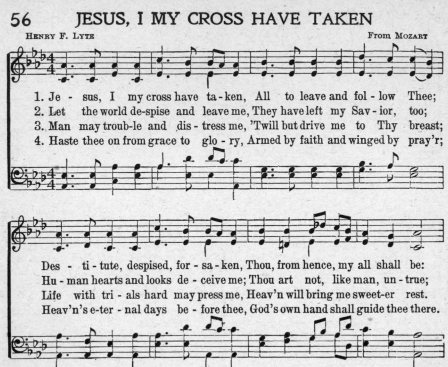

1. Je - sus, I my cross have ta - ken, All to leave and fol - low Thee;
2. Let the world de-spise and leave me, They have left my Sav - ior, too;
3. Man may troub-le and dis - tress me, 'Twill but drive me to Thy breast;
4. Haste thee on from grace to glo - ry, Armed by faith and winged by pray'r;

Des - ti - tute, despised, for - sa - ken, Thou, from hence, my all shall be:
Hu - man hearts and looks de - ceive me; Thou art not, like man, un - true;
Life with tri - als hard may press me, Heav'n will bring me sweet-er rest.
Heav'n's e-ter - nal days be - fore thee, God's own hand shall guide thee there.

Per - ish ev - 'ry fond am - bi - tion, All I've sought, and hoped, and known;
And, while Thou shalt smile up - on me, God of wis - dom, love, and might,
O 'tis not in grief to harm me, While Thy love is left to me;
Soon shall close thy earth - ly mission, Swift shall pass thy pil - grim days,

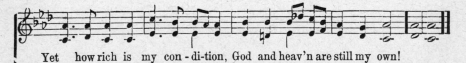

Yet how rich is my con - di - tion, God and heav'n are still my own!
Foes may hate and friends may shun me; Show Thy face, and all is bright.
O 'twere not in joy to charm me, Were that joy unmixed with Thee.
Hope shall change to glad fru-i - tion, Faith to sight, and pray'r to praise. A-men.

57 NO ONE EVER CARED FOR ME LIKE JESUS

C. F. W.   C. F. WEIGLE

1. I would love to tell you what I think of Je - sus Since I found in Him a
2. All my life was full of sin when Jesus found me, All my heart was full of
3. Ev - 'ry day He comes to me with new as-surance, More and more I un - der-

friend so strong and true; I would tell you how He changed my life completely,
mis - er - y and woe; Je - sus plac'd His strong and loving arms a - bout me,
stand His words of love; But I'll nev - er know just why He came to save me,

He did something that no oth - er friend could do.
And He led me in the way I ought to go.
Till some day I see His bless-ed face a - bove,

CHORUS

No one ev - er cared for me like Je - sus, There's no oth - er friend so kind as He; No one else could take the sin and darkness from me, O how much He cared for me.

58 HE PUT A SONG INTO MY HEART

C. A. M.   C. Austin Miles

1. A won-drous song was giv'n to me, 'Tis a mel-o-dy di-vine,
2. The song I sing was giv'n to me, When I knew my sins for-giv'n,
3. The song is mine, a gift of grace; But my Sav-iour will be-stow

So rich in heav-en's har-mo-ny, I re-joice to know it's mine.
Down at the foot of Cal-va-ry, When I caught a glimpse of Heav'n.
A song to all who seek His face, Who His pard'ning love would know.

Chorus *Not too fast*

He put a song, a won-der-ful song, in-to my heart, in-to my heart,

The sweetest mel-o-dy He gave to me. He put a song, a won-der-ful song,

in-to my heart, in-to my heart, He put a won-der-ful song in-to my heart.

GRACE GREATER THAN OUR SIN

Julia H. Johnston. D. B. Towner.

1. Mar - vel - ous grace of our lov - ing Lord, Grace that ex - ceeds our
2. Sin and de - spair like the sea waves cold, Threat - en the soul with
3. Dark is the stain that we can - not hide, What can a - vail to
4. Mar - vel - ous, in - fi - nite, match - less grace, Free - ly bestowed on

sin and our guilt, Yon - der on Cal - va - ry's mount out - poured,
in - fi - nite loss; Grace that is great - er, yes, grace un - told,
wash it a - way? Look, there is flow - ing a crim - son tide;
all who be - lieve; You that are long - ing to see His face,

CHORUS.

There where the blood of the Lamb was spilt. Grace, grace,
Points to the Ref - uge, the Might - y Cross.
Whit - er than snow you may be to - day.
Will you this mo - ment His grace re - ceive? Mar - vel - ous grace,

God's grace, Grace that will par-don and cleanse with-in; Grace
In - fi - nite grace, Mar - vel - ous

grace, God's grace, Grace that is great-er than all our sin.
grace, In - fi - nite grace,

60 IN REMEMBRANCE

Julia Benson Parker

B. D. Ackley

1. In re-mem-brance, Lord, I come, Be-fore Thy ta-ble spread;
2. Bless the sa-cred bread and cup Of which I now par-take;

Of Thy bod-y pierced for me, Thy blood so free-ly shed. . . .
free-ly shed.
Take my heart, 'tis all I have To give for Thy sweet sake. . . .
Thy sweet sake.

Though un-wor-thy, Lord, am I, Grant me Thy pard'ning grace,
Break to me the bread of Life, My hun-gry soul to feed;

And take a-way the sin that hides From me Thy glo-rious face.
And keep me close and true to Thee Till Thou re-turn in-deed.

61 MUST JESUS BEAR THE CROSS ALONE?

Thomas Shepherd

George N. Allen

1. Must Je-sus bear the cross a-lone, And all the world go free?
2. How hap-py are the saints a-bove, Who once went sor-rowing here!
3. The con-se-cra-ted cross I'll bear, Till death shall set me free;
4. Up-on the crys-tal pavement, down At Je-sus' pierc-ed feet,

MUST JESUS BEAR THE CROSS ALONE?

No, there's a cross for ev - 'ry one, And there's a cross for me.
But now they taste un - min - gled love, And joy with-out a tear.
And then go home my crown to wear, For there's a crown for me.
Joy - ful, I'll cast my gold - en crown, And His dear name re - peat.

62   NEAR THE CROSS

COPYRIGHT, 1890, BY W. H. DOANE

Fanny J. Crosby   W. H. Doane

1. Je - sus, keep me near the cross,   There a pre - cious foun - tain
2. Near the cross, a trem-bling soul,   Love and mer - cy found me;
3. Near the cross! O Lamb of God,   Bring its scenes be - fore me;
4. Near the cross I'll watch and wait,   Hop - ing, trust-ing ev - er,

Free to all— a heal - ing stream, Flows from Cal-v'ry's moun - tain.
There the Bright and Morn - ing Star Sheds its beams a - round me.
Help me walk from day to day, With its shad - ows o'er me.
Till I reach the gold - en strand, Just be - yond the riv - er.

CHORUS

In the cross, in the cross, Be my glo - ry ev - er;

Till my rap-tured soul shall find Rest be - yond the riv - er.

63 SINCE JESUS CAME INTO MY HEART

R. H. McDaniel   Chas. H. Gabriel

1. What a won-der-ful change in my life has been wrought Since Je-sus came
2. I have ceased from my wand'ring and go-ing a-stray, Since Je-sus came
3. I'm possessed of a hope that is stead-fast and sure, Since Je-sus came
4. There's a light in the val-ley of death now for me, Since Je-sus came
5. I shall go there to dwell in that cit-y I know, Since Je-sus came

in-to my heart; I have light in my soul for which long I had sought.
in-to my heart; And my sins which were ma-ny are all washed a-way,
in-to my heart; And no dark clouds of doubt now my path-way ob-scure,
in-to my heart; And the gates of the cit-y be-yond I can see,
in-to my heart; And I'm hap-py, so hap-py, as on-ward I go,

Chorus

Since Je-sus came in-to my heart.
Since Je-sus came in, came

Since Je-sus came in-to my
Since Je-sus came in, came

heart, Since Je-sus came in-to my heart; Floods of joy o'er my
in-to my heart, Since Je-sus came in, came in-to my heart;

soul like the sea - bil-lows roll, Since Je-sus came in-to my heart.

KEEP ON PRAYING

64

I. P. W.

Ina Pearle Whaley

1. Keep on pray-ing when the skies are gray, In God's pres-ence clouds will
2. Keep on pray-ing when the path grows dim, He will guide you if you
3. Keep on pray-ing for the soul a-stray, Lost in dark-ness, far from
4. Keep on pray-ing, prayer is not in vain, Day by day new vic-t'ries

break a-way; Keep on pray-ing till the sun shines thru, For
look to Him; Light from heav-en He will sure-ly send, For
Love's bright way, Ask for help the wan-d'ring one to win, For
you will gain; More like Je-sus you will ev-er grow, For

Chorus

God an-swers prayer. Keep on pray-ing, God is ev-er near;

Keep on pray-ing, He will sure-ly hear (If you will) Keep on pray-ing,

keep on trust-ing, too, Keep on pray-ing, God will an-swer you.

65 GROWING DEARER EACH DAY

C. H. G.

Chas. H. Gabriel

1. How sweet is the love of my Sav-iour! 'Tis bound-less and deep as the sea;
2. I know He is ev-er be-side me! E- ter - ni- ty on-ly will prove
3. Wher-ev - er He leads I will fol-low, Thru sor - row, or shad-ow, or sun;
4. Some day face to face I shall see Him, And oh, what a joy it will be

And best of it all, it is dai - ly Grow-ing sweeter and sweeter to me.
The height and the depth of His mercy, And the breadth of His in-fi-nite love.
And though I be tried in the fur-nace, I can say, "Lord, Thy will be it done."
To know that His love, now so precious, Will for - ev - er grow sweeter to me!

CHORUS

Sweet - - er and sweet-er to me, ... Dear - - er and
Sweet-er to me, grow - ing sweet-er to me, Dear-er each day,

dear - er each day; . . . . Oh, won - - der-ful love of my
grow - ing dear - er each day; Oh, won-der-ful love, love of my

Sav - iour, Grow-ing dear - - - er each step of my way!
Sav - iour, Grow-ing dear-er and dear-er each step of my way!

WE HAVE AN ANCHOR

Priscilla J. Owens

Wm. J. Kirkpatrick

1. Will your an-chor hold in the storms of life, When the
2. It is safe-ly moored, 'twill the storm with-stand, For 'tis
3. It will firm-ly hold in the straits of fear, When the
4. When our eyes be-hold thru the gath-'ring night The

clouds un-fold their wings of strife? When the strong tides lift, and the
well se-cured by the Sav-iour's hand; And the ca-bles, passed from His
breakers have told the reef is near; Though the tem-pest rage and the
cit-y of gold, our har-bor bright, We shall an-chor fast by the

ca-bles strain, Will your an-chor drift, or firm re-main?
heart to mine, Can de-fy the blast, thru strength di-vine.
wild winds blow, Not an an-gry wave shall our bark o'er-flow.
heav'n-ly shore, With the storms all past for-ev-er-more.

REFRAIN

We have an an-chor that keeps the soul Steadfast and sure while the billows roll,

Fastened to the Rock which cannot move, Grounded firm and deep in the Saviour's love.

67 STAND UP, STAND UP FOR JESUS

George Duffield

Adam Geibel

SOLO OR UNISON

1. Stand up, stand up for Je - sus, Ye sol-diers of the cross; Lift high His roy-al
2. Stand up, stand up for Je - sus, The trump-et call o - bey, Forth to the mighty
3. Stand up, stand up for Je - sus, Stand in His strength alone; The arm of flesh will
4. Stand up, stand up for Je - sus, The strife will not be long; This day the noise of

ban - ner, It must not suf-fer loss; From vic-t'ry un - to vic-t'ry His ar-my
con - flict, In this His glo-rious day; "Ye that are men now serve Him" Against un-
fail you, Ye dare not trust your own; Put on the gos-pel ar - mor, Each piece put
bat - tle, The next, the victor's song: To him that o - ver - com - eth, A crown of

rit.

shall He lead, Till ev'-ry foe is vanquished And Christ is Lord in - deed.
numbered foes; Let cour-age rise with dan - ger, And strength to strength oppose.
on with prayer; Where du-ty calls or dan - ger, Be nev - er want-ing there.
life shall be; He with the King of glo - ry Shall reign e - ter - nal - ly.

CHORUS *Harmony*

Stand up   for Je - sus, Ye sol - diers of the cross; .. Lift
    stand up

high His roy - al ban - ner, It must not, it must not suf - fer loss.

ARE YE ABLE, SAID THE MASTER

Earl Marlatt

Harry S. Mason

1. "Are ye a - ble," said the Mas - ter, "To be cru - ci - fied with me?"
2. "Are ye a - ble," to re - mem - ber, When a thief lifts up his eyes,
3. "Are ye a - ble," when the shad - ows Close a - round you with the sod,
4. "Are ye a - ble," still the Mas - ter Whis-pers down e - ter - ni - ty,

"Yea," the stur - dy dream-ers an-swered, "To the death we fol - low Thee."
That His par-doned soul is wor - thy Of a place in Par - a - dise?
To be - lieve that spir - it tri - umphs, To commend your soul to God?
And he - ro - ic spir - its an - swer, Now, as then in Gal - i - lee.

REFRAIN

"Lord, we are a - ble," Our spir - its are Thine, Re - mold them,

make us like Thee, di - vine. Thy guid - ing ra - diance a - bove

us shall be A bea - con to God, To love and loy - al - ty.

JESUS IS THE JOY OF LIVING

A. H. A.

Rev. A. H. Ackley

1. I have found a won-drous Sav-iour, Je-sus Christ, The Soul's De-light;
2. Life is grow-ing rich with beau-ty, Toil has lost its wea-ry strain,
3. Heav'nly wis-dom He pro-vides me, Grace to keep my spir-it free;
4. O what splen-dor, O what glo-ry, O what match-less pow'r di-vine,

Ev-'ry bless-ing of His fa-vor Fills my heart with hope so bright.
Now a ha-lo crowns each du-ty, And I sing a glad re-frain.
In His own sweet way He guides me When the path I can-not see.
Is the Christ of Gos-pel sto-ry, Christ, the Sav-iour, who is mine.

CHORUS

Je-sus is the Joy of Liv-ing, He's the King of Life to me; . . . . .
of Life to me;

Un-to Him my all I'm giv-ing, His for-ev-er-more to be (to be).

I will do what He com-mands me, An-y-where He leads I'll go (I'll go);

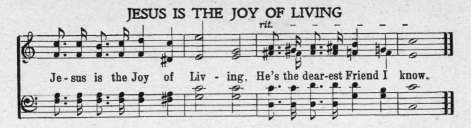

JESUS IS THE JOY OF LIVING

rit.

Je-sus is the Joy of Liv - ing, He's the dear-est Friend I know.

70 THE WORLD NEEDS A FRIEND LIKE JESUS

Rev. A. H. Ackley   Herbert G. Tovey

1. The world needs a friend like Je - sus, To save it from dark de - spair;
2. The world needs a friend like Je - sus, 'Tis wea - ry and worn and sad;
3. The world needs a friend like Je - sus, The rule of His scep-tered sway;
4. The world needs a friend like Je - sus, He's all that it needs and more,

The cure for its des - o - la - tion Is found in His lov - ing care. . .
The joy of His bless - ed pres - ence Is all that can make it glad. . .
The prob-lems of life will van - ish When Je-sus shall have His way. . .
And He will come in and save it When men o-pen wide the door. . .

CHORUS

The world needs a friend like Je - sus, The strong Son of God so true,

The world needs a friend like Je - sus, And no oth - er friend will do (will do).

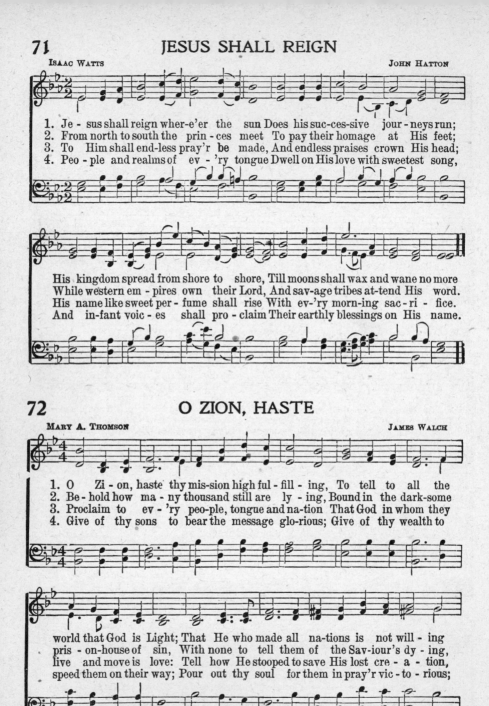

Isaac Watts   John Hatton

1. Je - sus shall reign wher-e'er the sun Does his suc-ces-sive jour-neys run;
2. From north to south the prin - ces meet To pay their homage at His feet;
3. To Him shall end-less pray'r be made, And endless praises crown His head;
4. Peo - ple and realms of ev - 'ry tongue Dwell on His love with sweetest song,

His kingdom spread from shore to shore, Till moons shall wax and wane no more
While western em - pires own their Lord, And sav-age tribes at-tend His word.
His name like sweet per - fume shall rise With ev-'ry morn-ing sac - ri - fice.
And in-fant voic - es shall pro - claim Their earthly blessings on His name.

72   O ZION, HASTE

Mary A. Thomson   James Walch

1. O Zi - on, haste thy mis-sion high ful - fill - ing, To tell to all the
2. Be - hold how ma - ny thousand still are ly - ing, Bound in the dark-some
3. Proclaim to ev - 'ry peo-ple, tongue and na-tion That God in whom they
4. Give of thy sons to bear the message glo-rious; Give of thy wealth to

world that God is Light; That He who made all na-tions is not will - ing
pris - on-house of sin, With none to tell them of the Sav-iour's dy - ing,
live and move is love: Tell how He stooped to save His lost cre - a - tion,
speed them on their way; Pour out thy soul for them in pray'r vic - to - rious;

O ZION, HASTE

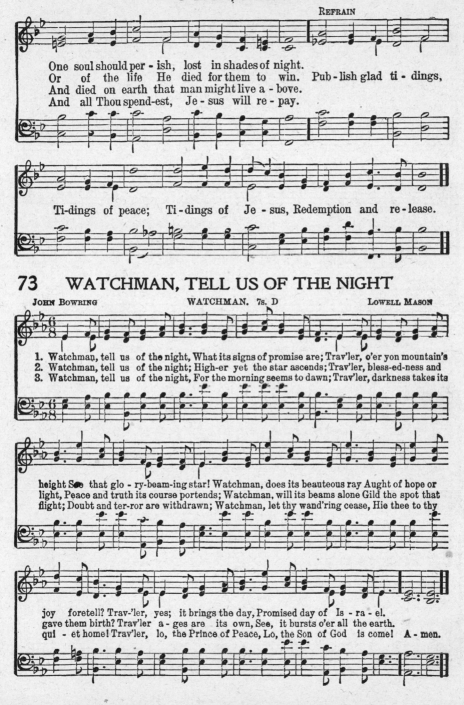

One soul should per - ish, lost in shades of night.
Or of the life He died for them to win. Pub - lish glad ti - dings,
And died on earth that man might live a - bove.
And all Thou spend-est, Je - sus will re - pay.

Ti-dings of peace; Ti-dings of Je - sus, Redemption and re - lease.

73 WATCHMAN, TELL US OF THE NIGHT

JOHN BOWRING   WATCHMAN. 7s. D   LOWELL MASON

1. Watchman, tell us of the night, What its signs of promise are; Trav'ler, o'er yon mountain's
2. Watchman, tell us of the night; High-er yet the star ascends; Trav'ler, bless-ed-ness and
3. Watchman, tell us of the night, For the morning seems to dawn; Trav'ler, darkness takes its

height See that glo - ry-beam-ing star! Watchman, does its beauteous ray Aught of hope or
light, Peace and truth its course portends; Watchman, will its beams alone Gild the spot that
flight; Doubt and ter-ror are withdrawn; Watchman, let thy wand'ring cease, Hie thee to thy

joy foretell? Trav-'ler, yes; it brings the day, Promised day of Is - ra - el.
gave them birth? Trav'ler a - ges are its own, See, it bursts o'er all the earth.
qui - et home! Trav'ler, lo, the Prince of Peace, Lo, the Son of God is come! A - men.

THE OLD RUGGED CROSS

Rev. George Bennard   Rev. George Bennard

1. On a hill far a - way stood an old rug-ged cross, The em-blem of
2. Oh, the old rug-ged cross, so de-spised by the world, Has a wondrous at-
3. In the old rug-ged cross, stained with blood so di-vine, A won - drous
4. To the old rug-ged cross I will ev - er be true, Its shame and re-

suf-f'ring and shame; And I love that old cross where the dear-est and best
trac-tion for me; For the dear Lamb of God left His glo - ry a - bove
beau - ty I see; For 'twas on that old cross Je - sus suf-fered and died
proach gladly bear; Then He'll call me some day to my home far a - way,

For a world of lost sin-ners was slain. So I'll cher-ish the old rug-ged
To bear it to dark Cal - va - ry.
To par-don and sanc-ti - fy me.
Where His glo-ry for - ev - er I'll share.

CHORUS

cross, the

cross, ... Till my tro-phies at last I lay down; I will cling to the
old rug-ged cross,

old rug - ged cross, ... And ex-change it some day for a crown.
cross, the old rug - ged cross,

75   HE IS MINE

C. Austin Miles   J. Lincoln Hall

1. There is a Shep-herd who cares for His own, And He is mine; Noth-ing am
2. Je - sus left heav-en my Sav-iour to be, And He is mine; I am not
3. There is a Com-fort - er come from a-bove, He, too, is mine; Com-ing to

I, He's a King on a throne, But He is mine; How He can love such a
worth all He suf-fered for me, But He is mine; Tho' I'm not wor-thy He
me to re - veal Je-sus' love, And that is mine; Shep-herd and Sav-iour, and

sin - ner as I, Tho' He is mine; I can-not fath-om tho' oft-en I try,
dwells in my heart, And He is mine; From Him I'll nev-er, no nev-er de-part,
Com-fort - er, too, They all are mine; That's why I know the old sto-ry is true,

CHORUS

But He is mine.
For He is mine.   He is mine, ... He
They all are mine.

He is mine,

Tho' all un - wor-thy, I know He is mine, He

is mine; Tho' it is won-der-ful, yet it is true, That He is mine.
yes, He is mine;

is mine;

76 MORE LOVE TO THEE

ELIZABETH PRENTISS   Used by permission   W. H. DOANE

1. More love to Thee, O Christ, More love to Thee! Hear Thou the
2. Once earth-ly joy I craved, Sought peace and rest; Now Thee a-
3. Then shall my lat-est breath Whis-per Thy praise; This be the

pray'r I make On bend-ed knee; This is my earn-est plea:
lone I seek, Give what is best; This all my pray'r shall be:
part-ing cry My heart shall raise; This still its pray'r shall be:

More love, O Christ, to Thee, More love to Thee, More love to Thee!

77 AMAZING GRACE

JOHN NEWTON

1. A - maz-ing grace! how sweet the sound, That saved a wretch like me! I
2. 'Twas grace that taught my heart to fear, And grace my fears re-lieved; How
3. Thro' man-y dan-gers, toils and snares, I have al-read-y come; 'Tis
4. When we've been there ten thousand years, Bright shining as the sun, We've

once was lost, but now am found, Was blind, but now I see.
pre-cious did that grace ap-pear The hour I first be-lieved!
grace hath bro't me safe thus far, And grace will lead me home.
no less days to sing God's praise Than when we first be-gun. A-men.

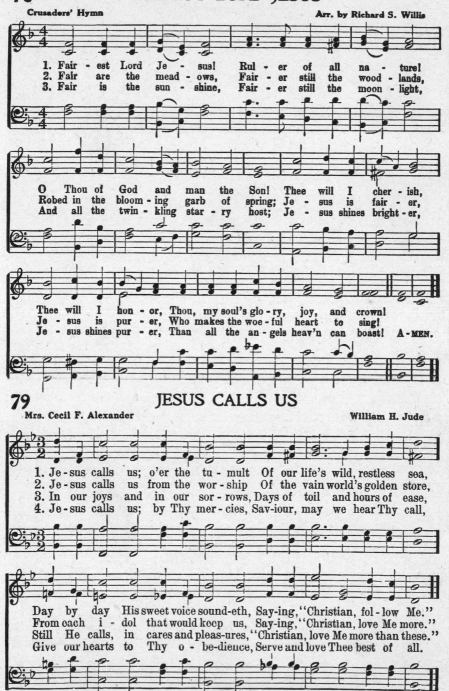

78 FAIREST LORD JESUS

Crusaders' Hymn

Arr. by Richard S. Willis

1. Fair-est Lord Je-sus! Rul-er of all na-ture!
2. Fair are the mead-ows, Fair-er still the wood-lands,
3. Fair is the sun-shine, Fair-er still the moon-light,

O Thou of God and man the Son! Thee will I cher-ish,
Robed in the bloom-ing garb of spring; Je-sus is fair-er,
And all the twin-kling star-ry host; Je-sus shines bright-er,

Thee will I hon-or, Thou, my soul's glo-ry, joy, and crown!
Je-sus is pur-er, Who makes the woe-ful heart to sing!
Je-sus shines pur-er, Than all the an-gels heav'n can boast! A-MEN.

79 JESUS CALLS US

Mrs. Cecil F. Alexander

William H. Jude

1. Je-sus calls us; o'er the tu-mult Of our life's wild, restless sea,
2. Je-sus calls us from the wor-ship Of the vain world's golden store,
3. In our joys and in our sor-rows, Days of toil and hours of ease,
4. Je-sus calls us; by Thy mer-cies, Sav-iour, may we hear Thy call,

Day by day His sweet voice sound-eth, Say-ing, "Christian, fol-low Me."
From each i-dol that would keep us, Say-ing, "Christian, love Me more."
Still He calls, in cares and pleas-ures, "Christian, love Me more than these."
Give our hearts to Thy o-be-dience, Serve and love Thee best of all.

80 IF JESUS GOES WITH ME

C. A. M.

WORDS AND MUSIC COPYRIGHT, 1936, RENEWAL
THE RODEHEAVER CO., OWNER

C. Austin Miles

1. It may be in the val-ley, where countless dangers hide; It may be in the
2. It may be I must car-ry the bless-ed word of life A-cross the burn-ing
3. But if it be my por-tion to bear my cross at home, While others bear their
4. It is not mine to ques-tion the judgments of my Lord, It is but mine to

sun-shine that I in peace a-bide; But this one thing I know— if
des-erts to those in sin-ful strife; And tho' it be my lot to
bur-dens be-yond the bil-lows' foam, I'll prove my faith in Him— con-
fol-low the lead-ings of His Word; But if to go or stay, or

it be dark or fair, If Je-sus is with me, I'll go an-y-where!
bear my col-ors there, If Je-sus goes with me, I'll go an-y-where!
fess His judgments fair, And, if He stays with me, I'll stay an-y-where!
wheth-er here or there, I'll be, with my Sav-iour, con-tent an-y-where!

CHORUS

If Je-sus goes with me, I'll go . . . an-y-where! 'Tis heav-en to me, Wher-
I'll go

e'er I may be, If He is there! I count it a priv-i-lege here His
His cross, His

cross to bear; .. If Je-sus goes with me, I'll go an - y - where.
cross, His cross to bear;

81   TRUSTING JESUS

E. Page   Ira D. Sankey

1. Sim - ply trust - ing ev - 'ry day, Trust-ing thru a storm-y way;
2. Bright-ly doth His Spir - it shine In - to this poor heart of mine;
3. Sing - ing if my way is clear; Pray-ing if the path be drear;
4. Trust-ing Him while life shall last, Trust-ing Him till earth be past;

E - ven when my faith is small, Trust-ing Je - sus, that is all.
While He leads I can - not fall; Trust-ing Je - sus, that is all.
If in dan - ger, for Him call; Trust-ing Je - sus, that is all.
Till with - in the jas - per wall: Trust-ing Je - sus, that is all.

CHORUS

Trust-ing as the mo-ments fly, Trust-ing as the days go by;

Trust-ing Him what-e'er be-fall, Trust-ing Je - sus, that is all.

O THOU IN WHOSE PRESENCE

Joseph Swain
Freeman Lewis

1. O Thou in whose pres-ence my soul takes de-light, On whom in af-flic-tion I call, My com-fort by day, and my song in the night, My hope, my sal-va-tion, my all!

2. Where dost Thou, dear Shep-herd, re-sort with Thy sheep, To feed them in pas-tures of love? Say, why in the val-ley of death should I weep, Or a-lone in this wil-der-ness rove?

3. O why should I wan-der an a-lien from Thee, Or cry in the des-ert for bread? Thy foes will re-joice when my sor-rows they see, And smile at the tears I have shed.

4. Ye daughters of Zi-on, de-clare, have you seen The star that on Is-ra-el shone? Say, if in your tents my Be-lov-ed has been, And where with His flocks He is gone.

83
JESUS, SAVIOUR, PILOT ME

Edward Hopper
J. E. Gould
FINE

1. Je-sus, Sav-iour, pi-lot me O-ver life's tem-pes-tuous sea;
D.C.—Chart and com-pass came from Thee, Je-sus, Sav-iour, pi-lot me.

2. As a moth-er stills her child, Thou canst hush the o-cean wild;
D.C.—Wondrous Sov-'reign of the sea; Je-sus, Sav-iour, pi-lot me.

3. When at last I near the shore, And the fear-ful break-ers roar
D.C.—May I hear Thee say to me: "Fear not, I will pi-lot thee."

Un-known waves a-round me roll, Hid-ing rock and treach'rous shoal;
Bois-t'rous waves o-bey Thy will When Thou say'st to them "be still!"
'Twixt me and the peace-ful rest, Then, while lean-ing on Thy breast,

84 'TIS SO SWEET TO TRUST IN JESUS

Louisa M. R. Stead

Wm. J. Kirkpatrick

1. 'Tis so sweet to trust in Je-sus, Just to take Him at His word;
2. O how sweet to trust in Je-sus, Just to trust His cleansing blood;
3. Yes, 'tis sweet to trust in Je-sus, Just from sin and self to cease;
4. I'm so glad I learned to trust Thee, Pre-cious Je-sus, Saviour, Friend;

Just to rest up-on His prom-ise; Just to know, "Thus saith the Lord."
Just in sim-ple faith to plunge me 'Neath the heal-ing, cleans-ing flood!
Just from Je-sus sim-ply tak-ing Life and rest, and joy and peace.
And I know that Thou art with me, Wilt be with me to the end.

CHORUS

Je-sus, Je-sus, how I trust Him! How I've proved Him o'er and o'er!

p

Je-sus, Je-sus, precious Je-sus! O for grace to trust Him more!

85 JESUS SET THE WORLD TO SINGING

A. H. A.

Rev. A. H. Ackley

1. There is mu-sic in the air, I can hear it ev-'ry-where, Je-sus
2. Hills and val-leys voice their praise, Birds and flow'rs their carols raise, Je-sus
3. Night re-peats the wondrous song, Moon and stars the strains prolong, Je-sus

set the world to singing when He came; Sons of men in tune-ful lay Love's sweet
set the world to singing when He came; Dawn and sun-set glo-ri-fy Him Who
set the world to singing when He came; Earth and sky with sweet accord Greet the

mel-o-dy dis-play, Je-sus set the world to sing-ing when He came.
reigns ex-alt-ed high, Je-sus set the world to sing-ing when He came.
com-ing of the Lord, Je-sus set the world to sing-ing when He came.

CHORUS

Je-sus set the world to sing-ing when He came, And the song is grow-ing

sweet-er, praise His name! Then take up the glad re-frain, Till the

JESUS SET THE WORLD TO SINGING

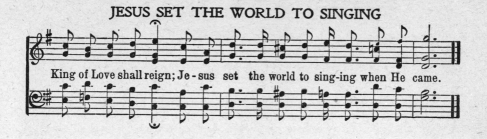

King of Love shall reign; Je-sus set the world to sing-ing when He came.

86 BEYOND THE SUNSET

(Dedicated to Horace L. and Grace Pierce Burr)

VIRGIL P. BROCK · BLANCHE KERR BROCK

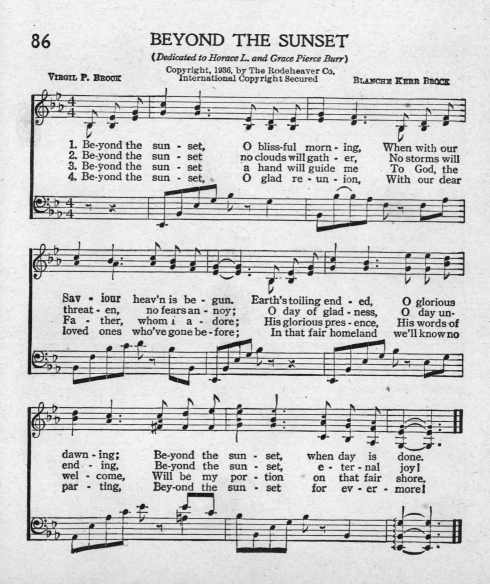

1. Be-yond the sun-set, O bliss-ful morn-ing, When with our
2. Be-yond the sun-set no clouds will gath-er, No storms will
3. Be-yond the sun-set a hand will guide me To God, the
4. Be-yond the sun-set, O glad re-un-ion, With our dear

Sav-iour heav'n is be-gun. Earth's toiling end-ed, O glorious
threat-en, no fears an-noy; O day of glad-ness, O day un-
Fa-ther, whom i a-dore; His glorious pres-ence, His words of
loved ones who've gone be-fore; In that fair homeland we'll know no

dawn-ing; Be-yond the sun-set, when day is done.
end-ing, Be-yond the sun-set, e-ter-nal joy!
wel-come, Will be my por-tion on that fair shore.
par-ting, Bey-ond the sun-set for ev-er-more!

87 WAITING ON JESUS

Oswald J. Smith

B. D. Ackley

1. Wait-ing on Je - sus when I am weak, Claim-ing His prom - ise
2. Wait-ing on Je - sus when I'm op - prest, Find - ing in Him sweet
3. Wait-ing on Je - sus lest I de - spair, Know-ing He ev - er

to those who seek; Wait-ing on Je - sus when I am strong, Trusting Him
com-fort and rest; Trust-ing Him ful - ly, what-e'er be-fall, Je - sus my
hear-eth my prayer; How can I doubt Him when He is near? No one so

CHORUS

on - ly all the day long.
Sav - iour, Je - sus my all.
lov - ing, no one so dear.

Wait-ing on Je - sus, rap-ture di-

vine! Won-der of won-ders, Je - sus is mine; . . . . Trust-ing and
He is mine;

pray - ing, what-e'er be - tide, Walk-ing each moment close by His side.

88 A REVIVAL HYMN

Rev. Oswald J. Smith

B. D. Ackley

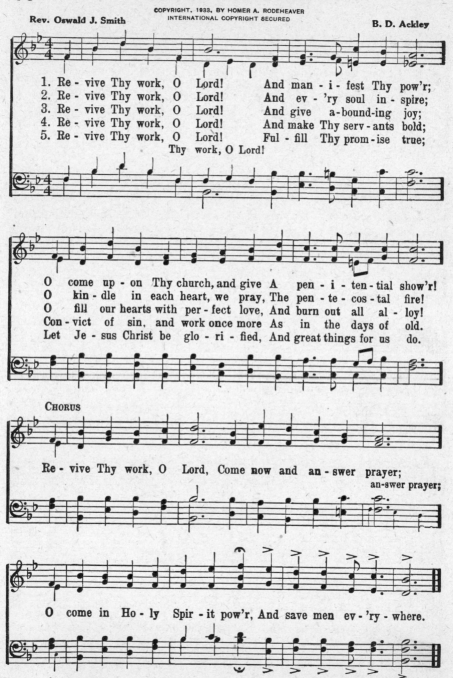

1. Re - vive Thy work, O Lord! And man - i - fest Thy pow'r;
2. Re - vive Thy work, O Lord! And ev - 'ry soul in - spire;
3. Re - vive Thy work, O Lord! And give a - bound-ing joy;
4. Re - vive Thy work, O Lord! And make Thy serv - ants bold;
5. Re - vive Thy work, O Lord! Ful - fill Thy prom - ise true;
Thy work, O Lord!

O come up - on Thy church, and give A pen - i - ten - tial show'r!
O kin - dle in each heart, we pray, The pen - te - cos - tal fire!
O fill our hearts with per - fect love, And burn out all al - loy!
Con - vict of sin, and work once more As in the days of old.
Let Je - sus Christ be glo - ri - fied, And great things for us do.

CHORUS

Re - vive Thy work, O Lord, Come now and an - swer prayer;
an - swer prayer;

O come in Ho - ly Spir - it pow'r, And save men ev - 'ry - where.

89 FOR GOD SO LOVED THE WORLD

E. E. Hewitt

J. Lincoln Hall

1. A sto - ry sweet and won - drous, Like heav'n-ly mu - sic swells;
2. When griev-ing, bro-ken-heart - ed, Be - cause of sin and shame,
3. This love, be - yond all meas - ure Of earth or sea or sky,

In chim-ings clear to all who will hear, Ring out the Gos - pel bells.
We find a joy earth can-not de-stroy, Be - liev-ing on His name.
Could on - ly show its full o - ver-flow, When Je - sus came to die.

CHORUS

For God so loved the world . . . that He gave His on - ly be-
For God . . . . so loved the world,

got - ten Son, that who - so - ev - er be - liev - eth in Him, who - so-

ev - er be - liev - eth in Him Should not per - ish, should not

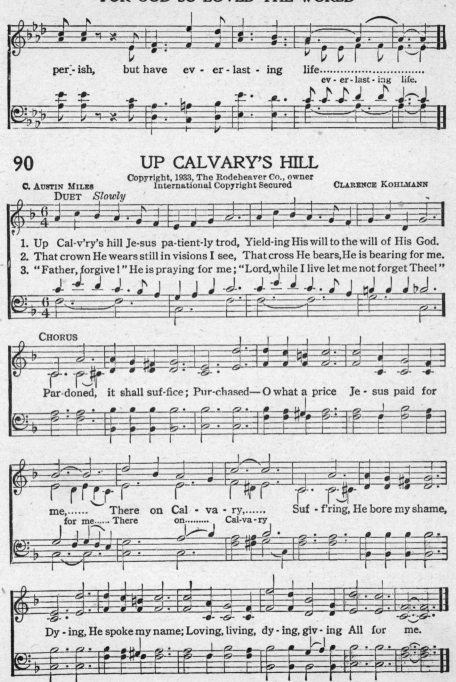

per-ish, but have ev-er-last-ing life.......................
ev-er-last-ing life.

90 UP CALVARY'S HILL

Copyright, 1933, The Rodeheaver Co., owner
International Copyright Secured

C. Austin Miles

Clarence Kohlmann

DUET *Slowly*

1. Up Cal-v'ry's hill Je-sus pa-tient-ly trod, Yield-ing His will to the will of His God.
2. That crown He wears still in visions I see, That cross He bears, He is bearing for me.
3. "Father, forgive!" He is praying for me; "Lord, while I live let me not forget Thee!"

CHORUS

Par-doned, it shall suf-fice; Pur-chased—O what a price Je-sus paid for

me,...... There on Cal-va-ry,...... Suf-f'ring, He bore my shame,
for me...... There on.......... Cal-va-ry

Dy-ing, He spoke my name; Loving, living, dy-ing, giv-ing All for me.

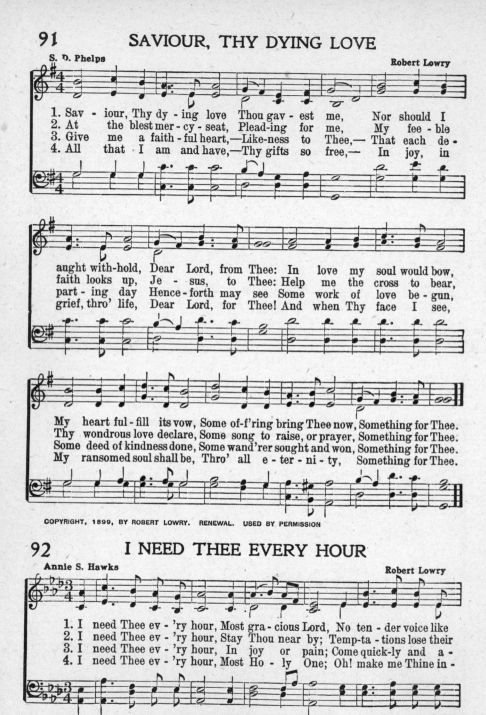

91 SAVIOUR, THY DYING LOVE

S. D. Phelps

Robert Lowry

1. Sav - iour, Thy dy - ing love Thou gav - est me, Nor should I
2. At the blest mer - cy - seat, Plead-ing for me, My fee - ble
3. Give me a faith - ful heart,—Like-ness to Thee,— That each de -
4. All that I am and have,—Thy gifts so free,— In joy, in

aught with-hold, Dear Lord, from Thee: In love my soul would bow,
faith looks up, Je - sus, to Thee: Help me the cross to bear,
part - ing day Hence-forth may see Some work of love be - gun,
grief, thro' life, Dear Lord, for Thee! And when Thy face I see,

My heart ful - fill its vow, Some of-f'ring bring Thee now, Something for Thee.
Thy wondrous love declare, Some song to raise, or prayer, Something for Thee.
Some deed of kindness done, Some wand'rer sought and won, Something for Thee.
My ransomed soul shall be, Thro' all e - ter - ni - ty, Something for Thee.

92 I NEED THEE EVERY HOUR

Annie S. Hawks

Robert Lowry

1. I need Thee ev - 'ry hour, Most gra - cious Lord, No ten - der voice like
2. I need Thee ev - 'ry hour, Stay Thou near by; Temp-ta - tions lose their
3. I need Thee ev - 'ry hour, In joy or pain; Come quick-ly and a -
4. I need Thee ev - 'ry hour, Most Ho - ly One; Oh! make me Thine in -

I NEED THEE EVERY HOUR
CHORUS

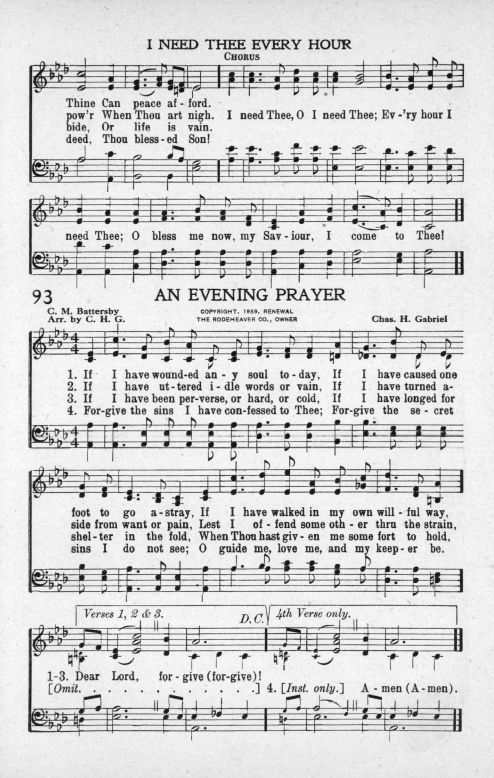

Thine Can peace af-ford.
pow'r When Thou art nigh. I need Thee, O I need Thee; Ev-'ry hour I
bide, Or life is vain.
deed, Thou bless-ed Son!

need Thee; O bless me now, my Sav-iour, I come to Thee!

93   AN EVENING PRAYER

C. M. Battersby
Arr. by C. H. G.

Chas. H. Gabriel

1. If I have wound-ed an-y soul to-day, If I have caused one
2. If I have ut-tered i-dle words or vain, If I have turned a-
3. If I have been per-verse, or hard, or cold, If I have longed for
4. For-give the sins I have con-fessed to Thee; For-give the se-cret

foot to go a-stray, If I have walked in my own will-ful way,
side from want or pain, Lest I of-fend some oth-er thru the strain,
shel-ter in the fold, When Thou hast giv-en me some fort to hold,
sins I do not see; O guide me, love me, and my keep-er be.

Verses 1, 2 & 3.   D.C.   4th Verse only.

1-3. Dear Lord, for-give (for-give)!
[Omit . . . .] 4. [Inst. only.] A-men (A-men).

THE GLORY OF HIS PRESENCE

Rev. Oswald J. Smith

B. D. Ackley

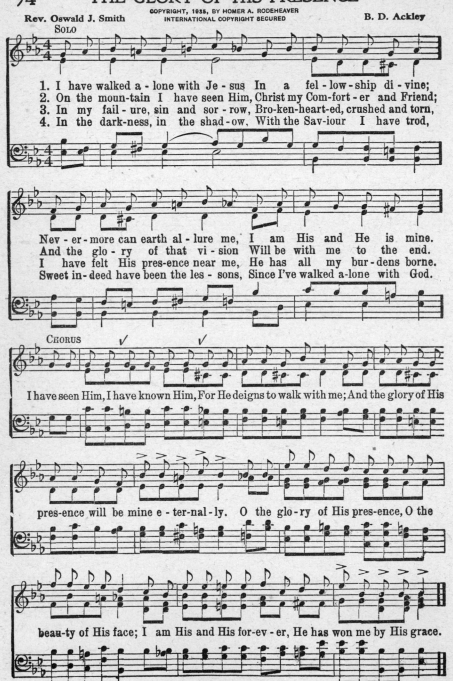

SOLO

1. I have walked a - lone with Je - sus In a fel - low - ship di - vine;
2. On the moun-tain I have seen Him, Christ my Com-fort - er and Friend;
3. In my fail - ure, sin and sor - row, Bro-ken-heart-ed, crushed and torn,
4. In the dark-ness, in the shad - ow, With the Sav-iour I have trod,

Nev - er - more can earth al - lure me, I am His and He is mine.
And the glo - ry of that vi - sion Will be with me to the end.
I have felt His pres-ence near me, He has all my bur - dens borne.
Sweet in - deed have been the les - sons, Since I've walked a-lone with God.

CHORUS

I have seen Him, I have known Him, For He deigns to walk with me; And the glory of His

pres-ence will be mine e - ter-nal - ly. O the glo-ry of His pres-ence, O the

beau-ty of His face; I am His and His for-ev - er, He has won me by His grace.

95 THE BEAUTIFUL GARDEN OF PRAYER

ELEANOR ALLEN SCHROLL   J. H. FILLMORE

1. There's a gar-den where Je-sus is wait-ing, There's a place that is won-drous-ly fair; For it glows with the light of His pres-ence, 'Tis the beau-ti-ful gar-den of pray'r.

2. There's a gar-den where Je-sus is wait-ing, And I go with my bur-den and care, Just to learn from His lips words of com-fort, In the beau-ti-ful gar-den of pray'r.

3. There's a gar-den where Je-sus is wait-ing, And He bids you to come meet Him there; Just to bow and re-ceive a new bless-ing, In the beau-ti-ful gar-den of pray'r.

REFRAIN

O the beau-ti-ful gar-den, the garden of pray'r, O the beau-ti-ful gar-den of pray'r; There my Sav-iour a-waits, and He o-pens the gates To the beau-ti-ful gar-den of pray'r.

96 THE GOLDEN KEY

John Parker

Jno. R. Sweney

1. Pray-er is the key For the bend-ing knee To o-pen the morn's first hours,
2. Not a soul so sad, Nor a heart so glad, When com-eth the shades of night;

See the in-cense rise To the star-ry skies, Like per-fume from the flow'rs.
But the day-break song Will the joy pro-long, And dark-ness turn to light.

97 TAKE TIME TO BE HOLY

W. D. Longstaff

Geo. C. Stebbins

1. Take time to be ho-ly, Speak oft with thy Lord; A-bide in Him
2. Take time to be ho-ly, The world rush-es on; Spend much time in
3. Take time to be ho-ly, Let Him be thy Guide; And run not be-

al-ways, And feed on His Word. Make friends of God's chil-dren,
se-cret With Je-sus a-lone— By look-ing to Je-sus,
fore Him, What-ev-er be-tide. In joy or in sor-row,

Help those who are weak; For-get-ting in noth-ing His bless-ing to seek.
Like Him thou shalt be; Thy friends, in thy conduct His like-ness shall see.
Still fol-low thy Lord, And, look-ing to Je-sus, Still trust in His Word.

98 **MY FAITH LOOKS UP TO THEE**

RAY PALMER

LOWELL MASON

1. My faith looks up to Thee, Thou Lamb of Cal-va-ry, Sav-ior di-vine; Now hear me
2. May Thy rich grace impart Strength to my fainting heart, My zeal in-spire; As Thou hast
3. While life's dark maze I tread, And griefs around me spread, Be Thou my Guide; Bid darkness

when I pray, Take all my sin a-way, O let me from this day Be whol-ly Thine!
died for me, O may my love to Thee, Pure, warm, and changeless be,—A liv-ing fire!
turn to day, Wipe sorrow's tears a-way, Nor let me ev-er stray From Thee a-side.

99 **MY JESUS, I LOVE THEE**

ANONYMOUS

A. J. GORDON

1. My Je-sus, I love Thee, I know Thou art mine, For Thee all the
2. I'll love Thee in life, I will love Thee in death, And praise Thee as
3. In mansions of glo-ry and end-less de-light, I'll ev-er a-

pleas-ures of sin I re-sign; My gra-cious Re-deem-er, my
long as Thou lend-est me breath; And say when the death-dew lies
dore Thee in heav-en so bright; I'll sing with the glit-ter-ing

Sav-iour art Thou; If ev-er I loved Thee, my Je-sus, 'tis now.
cold on my brow, If ev-er I loved Thee, my Je-sus, 'tis now.
crown on my brow, If ev-er I loved Thee, my Je-sus, 'tis now.

WIN THEM ONE BY ONE

C. A. M.

C. AUSTIN MILES

In march time

1. If to Christ our on-ly King Men redeemed we strive to bring,
2. Side by side we stand each day Saved are we, but lost are they;
3. On-ly cow-ards dare re-fuse, Dare this gift of God mis-use;

Just one way may this be done—We must win them one by one.
They will come if we but dare Speak a word back'd up by pray'r,
Ere some friend goes to his grave, Speak a word his soul to save.

CHORUS

So, you bring the one next to you, And I'll bring the one next to me; In
If you'll bring the one next to you, And I bring the one next to me; In

1

all kinds of weather we'll all work togeth-er, And see what can be done, In

2

no time at all we'll have them all, So win them, win them one by one.

AMERICA THE BEAUTIFUL

KATHARINE LEE BATES   SAMUEL A. WARD

1. O beau-ti-ful for spa-cious skies, For am-ber waves of grain; ...
2. O beau-ti-ful for pil-grim feet, Whose stern, im-pas-sioned stress ...
3. O beau-ti-ful for he-roes proved In lib-er-at-ing strife, ...
4. O beau-ti-ful for pa-triot dream That sees be-yond the years ....

For pur-ple moun-tain maj-es-ties A-bove the fruit-ed plain!
A thor-ough-fare for free-dom beat A-cross the wil-der-ness!
Who more than self their coun-try loved, And mer-cy more than life!
Thine al-a-bas-ter cit-ies gleam Un-dimmed by hu-man tears!

A-mer-i-ca! A-mer-i-ca! God shed His grace on thee,
A-mer-i-ca! A-mer-i-ca! God mend thine ev-'ry flaw,
A-mer-i-ca! A-mer-i-ca! May God thy gold re-fine
A-mer-i-ca! A-mer-i-ca! God shed His grace on thee,

And crown thy good with broth-er-hood From sea to shin-ing sea!
Con-firm thy soul in self-con-trol, Thy lib-er-ty in law!
Till all suc-cess be no-ble-ness, And ev-'ry gain di-vine!
And crown thy good with broth-er-hood From sea to shin-ing sea!

102 JESUS SET THE MUSIC RINGING

Rev. George O. Webster

C. Austin Miles

1. You ask what makes me hap-py The whole day long, Why I am al-ways
2. I can-not keep from sing-ing Since that glad day, When Je-sus took, in
3. His love each day is grow-ing More sweet to me, Each day new grace and

sing-ing A glad-some song; Ah, well do I re-mem-ber When
mer-cy, My sins a-way; He o-pened up a foun-tain Whence
beau-ty In Him I see; For all this world can of-fer From

song be-gan to start, 'Twas Je-sus set the mu-sic Ring-ing in my heart.
streams of gladness start, 'Twas Je-sus set the mu-sic Ring-ing in my heart.
Him I would not part, Since He has set the mu-sic Ring-ing in my heart.

CHORUS

In my heart . . . He set the mu-sic ringing, In my life . . . . a heav'n-ly

In my heart   In my life

glad-ness bringing; Ah, well do I re-mem-ber When song be-gan to start,

JESUS SET THE MUSIC RINGING

'Twas Je - sus set the mu - sic Ring-ing in my heart.
Ring-ing, ring - ing in my heart.

103   **HEAVENLY SUNLIGHT**

Rev. H. J. Zelley   COPYRIGHT, 1899, BY H. L. GILMOUR   G. H. Cook

1. Walk-ing in sun-light, all of my jour-ney, O - ver the moun-tains,
2. Shad-ows a - round me, shad-ows a - bove me, Nev - er con-ceal my
3. In the bright sun-light, ev - er re-joic-ing, Press-ing my way to

thru the deep vale; Je - sus has said, "I'll nev - er for-sake thee," Prom-ise di-
Sav-iour and Guide; He is the light, in Him is no dark-ness, Ev - er I'm
man-sions a - bove; Singing His prais-es, glad-ly I'm walk-ing, Walk-ing in

D. S.—Sing-ing His

FINE   CHORUS

vine that nev - er shall fail.
walk-ing close to His side.   Heav-en-ly sun-light, heav-en-ly sun-light,
sun - light, sun-light of love.

prais - es, Je - sus is mine.   D. S.

Flood-ing my soul with glo-ry di - vine; Hal-le - lu - jah! I am re-joic-ing,

JESUS TOOK MY BURDEN

Rev. Johnson Oatman, Jr.

Bertha Mae Lillenas

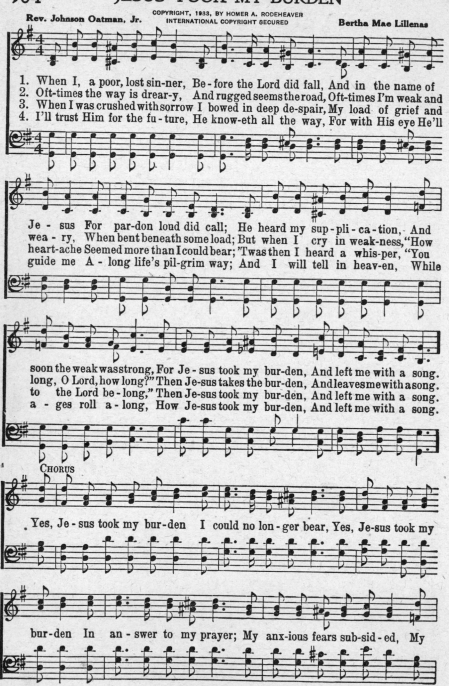

1. When I, a poor, lost sin-ner, Be-fore the Lord did fall, And in the name of
2. Oft-times the way is drear-y, And rugged seems the road, Oft-times I'm weak and
3. When I was crushed with sorrow I bowed in deep de-spair, My load of grief and
4. I'll trust Him for the fu-ture, He know-eth all the way, For with His eye He'll

Je - sus For par-don loud did call; He heard my sup-pli-ca-tion, And
wea - ry, When bent beneath some load; But when I cry in weak-ness, "How
heart-ache Seemed more than I could bear; 'Twas then I heard a whis-per, "You
guide me A - long life's pil-grim way; And I will tell in heav-en, While

soon the weak was strong, For Je - sus took my bur-den, And left me with a song.
long, O Lord, how long?" Then Je-sus takes the bur-den, And leaves me with a song.
to the Lord be-long," Then Je-sus took my bur-den, And left me with a song.
a - ges roll a-long, How Je-sus took my bur-den, And left me with a song.

CHORUS

Yes, Je-sus took my bur-den I could no lon-ger bear, Yes, Je-sus took my

bur-den In an-swer to my prayer; My anx-ious fears sub-sid-ed, My

JESUS TOOK MY BURDEN

spir-it was made strong, For Je-sus took my bur-den, And left me with a song.

105 HE LIFTED ME

Charlotte G. Homer   Chas. H. Gabriel

1. In lov-ing kind-ness Je-sus came, My soul in mer - cy to re-claim,
2. He called me long be - fore I heard, Be-fore my sin-ful heart was stirred,
3. His brow was pierced with man-y a thorn, His hands by cru - el nails were torn,
4. Now on a high - er plane I dwell, And with my soul I know 'tis well;

And from the depths of sin and shame Thro' grace He lift - ed me. . . . . . .
But when I took Him at His word, For-giv'n He lift - ed me. . . . . . .
When from my guilt and grief, for-lorn, In love He lift - ed me. . . . . . .
Yet how or why, I can-not tell, He should have lift - ed me. . . . . .

He lift-ed me.

Chorus

From sink-ing sand He lift - ed me, With ten-der hand He lift - ed me,

From shades of night to planes of light, O praise His name, He lift-ed me!

106 O JESUS, I HAVE PROMISED

John E. Bode ANGEL'S STORY 7. 6. 7. 6. D. Arthur H. Mann

1. O Je-sus, I have promised To serve Thee to the end; Be Thou forever near me,
2. Oh! let me feel Thee near me; The world is ever near. I see the sights that dazzle,
3. O Jesus, Thou hast promised To all who follow Thee, That where Thou art in glo-ry

My Mas-ter and my Friend: I shall not fear the bat - tle If Thou art by my side,
The tempting sounds I hear. My foes are ev - er near me, Around me and within;
There shall Thy servant be; And, Jesus, I have promised To serve Thee to the end.

Nor wan - der from the path - way If Thou wilt be my guide.
But, Je - sus, draw Thou near - er, And shield my soul from sin.
Oh! give me grace to fol - low, My Mas - ter and my Friend. A - men.

107 HE CARES FOR ME

Anonymous J. R. Murray

1. How strong and sweet my Father's care, That round a-bout me, like the air,
2. The tho't great won-der with it brings, My cares are all such lit - tle things,
3. O keep me ev - er in Thy love, Dear Fa-ther, watching from a-bove,

Is with me al - ways, ev - 'ry - where! He cares for me.
But to the truth my glad heart clings, He cares for me.
And as thru life my steps shall move, O care for me.

108 O JESUS, THOU ART STANDING

William W. How

Justin H. Knecht

1. O Je - sus, Thou art standing Out-side the fast-closed door, In low - ly
2. O Je - sus, Thou art knocking; And lo, that hand is scarred, And thorns Thy
3. O Je - sus, Thou art pleading In ac-cents meek and low, "I died for

patience waiting To pass the threshold o'er: Shame on us, Christian brothers, His
brow en-cir - cle, And tears Thy face have marred: O love that passeth knowledge, So
you, my children, And will you treat Me so?" O Lord, with shame and sorrow We

name and sign who bear, O shame, thrice shame upon us, To keep Him standing there!
pa - tient-ly to wait! O sin that hath no e-qual, So fast to bar the gate!
o - pen now the door; Dear Saviour, en-ter, en - ter, And leave us nev-er-more.

109 YOU MUST BELIEVE

A. H. A. Rev. A. H. Ackley

1. You can know Je-sus and love Him to-day, You must be-lieve, there is
2. Knowledge will come of His bless-ings so sweet, When in sub-mis-sion you
3. Christ, the Unknown, He will still be to you, Till you have done what He

no oth-er way; This is the se-cret of prov-ing His claim,
bow at His feet; His liv-ing pres-ence your be-ing will thrill
tells you to do; Fol-low, o-bey Him, He asks noth-ing more,

Chorus

Find-ing sal-va-tion from sin thru His name.
When you sur-ren-der your life to His will. You must be-lieve, you must
And you will know Him as nev-er be-fore.

trust Him, and then You will know Je-sus, the Sav-iour of men; Proof you are

rit.

seek-ing you then will re-ceive, You can know Je-sus, but you must be-lieve.

110 HEARTACHES

A. H. A.

COPYRIGHT, 1938, BY ACKLEY & SCHOFIELD
HOMER A. RODEHEAVER, OWNER

Rev. A. H. Ackley

1. When your heart is ach-ing, turn to Je-sus, He's the dear-est
2. There is joy for ev-'ry blight-ing sor-row, Sweet re-lief for
3. Je-sus un-der-stands, what-e'er the trou-ble, And He waits to

Friend that you can know; You will find Him standing close beside you,
ev-'ry bit-ter pain, Je-sus Christ is still the great Phy-si-cian,
heal your wound-ed soul; Will you trust His love so strong and tender,

Chorus

Wait-ing peace and com-fort to be-stow. . . .
No one ev-er sought His help in vain. . . . Heart-aches, take them all to
He a-lone can make your spir-it whole. . . .

Je-sus, Go to Him to-day, do it now with-out de-lay; Heart-aches,

take them all to Je-sus, He will take your heartaches all a-way.
He will take them all a-way.

111 SAVIOUR, MORE THAN LIFE

FANNY J. CROSBY   COPYRIGHT, 1903, BY W. H. DOANE   W. H. DOANE

1. Sav-iour. more than life to me, I am clinging, clinging close to Thee;
2. Thro' this changing world be - low, Lead me gen-tly, gen-tly as I go;
3. Let me love Thee more and more, Till this fleeting, fleeting life is o'er,

Let Thy pre-cious blood ap-plied; Keep me ev - er, ev - er near Thy side.
Trusting Thee, I can-not stray, I can nev-er, nev-er lose my way.
Till my soul is lost in love, In a brighter, brighter world a - bove.

D. S.—*May Thy ten - der love to me*   *Bind me clos - er, clos - er, Lord, to Thee.*

REFRAIN   D. S.

Ev-'ry day, ev-'ry hour, Let me feel Thy cleansing pow'r;
Ev - 'ry day and hour, Ev - 'ry day and hour,

112 HOLY SPIRIT, WITH LIGHT DIVINE

Andrew Reed   Louis Gottschalk

1. Ho - ly Sp' -it, with light di - vine, Shine up - on this heart of mine;
2. Ho - ly Spir-it, with pow'r di - vine Cleanse this guilt - y heart of mine;
3. Ho - ly Spir-it, with joy di - vine, Cheer this sad-dened heart of mine;
4. Ho - ly Spir - it, all di - vin , Dwell with - in this heart of mine;

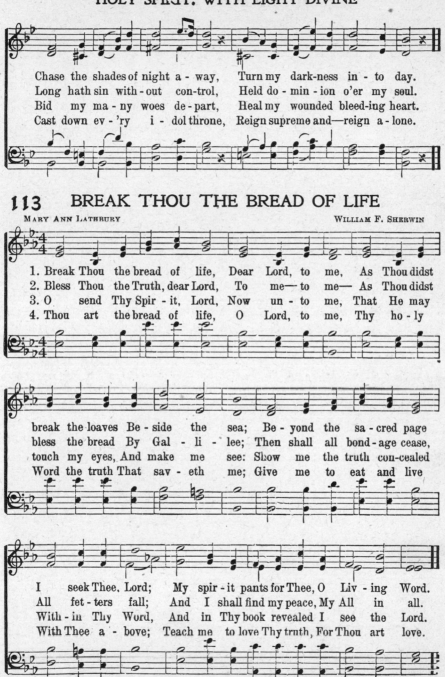

Chase the shades of night a - way, Turn my dark-ness in - to day.
Long hath sin with - out con-trol, Held do - min - ion o'er my soul.
Bid my ma - ny woes de - part, Heal my wounded bleed-ing heart.
Cast down ev - 'ry i - dol throne, Reign supreme and—reign a - lone.

113 BREAK THOU THE BREAD OF LIFE

MARY ANN LATHBURY

WILLIAM F. SHERWIN

1. Break Thou the bread of life, Dear Lord, to me, As Thou didst
2. Bless Thou the Truth, dear Lord, To me— to me— As Thou didst
3. O send Thy Spir - it, Lord, Now un - to me, That He may
4. Thou art the bread of life, O Lord, to me, Thy ho - ly

break the loaves Be - side the sea; Be - yond the sa - cred page
bless the bread By Gal - li - lee; Then shall all bond - age cease,
touch my eyes, And make me see: Show me the truth con-cealed
Word the truth That sav - eth me; Give me to eat and live

I seek Thee, Lord; My spir - it pants for Thee, O Liv - ing Word.
All fet - ters fall; And I shall find my peace, My All in all.
With - in Thy Word, And in Thy book revealed I see the Lord.
With Thee a - bove; Teach me to love Thy truth, For Thou art love.

114 SUNSHINE IN THE RAIN

A. H. A.   Rev. A. H. Ackley

1. There are storm-y days of trou-ble that are hard to un-derstand, When the
2. There are times of sore af-flic-tion when our broken heart cries out, "Why, O
3. Ev - 'ry- thing reveals God's goodness, ev - 'ry bur-den that we bear, Ev -'ry

heart grows sick with nameless fear and dread, When the darkness of the
God, hast Thou for-got-ten to be kind?" When the fu - ry of dis -
cir - cum-stance is mingled with His love, There's a lit - tle bit of

temp-est seems to hide God's lov - ing hand, And the rains of woe beat
as - ter o - ver-whelms our soul with doubt, And the ques-tion of His
heav - en in the most per-plex- ing care, God has temp-ered it with

down up - on our head.
good-ness fills our mind. } There's a lit - tle of God's sun-shine in the rain,
mer - cy from a - bove.

CHORUS

There's a lit - tle of His goodness in the pain, There's a lit - tle of His

SUNSHINE IN THE RAIN

love, in the darkest cloud above, There's a lit-tle of God's sunshine in the rain.

115   DEAR LORD, FORGIVE

CHARLOTTE G. HOMER   CHAS. H. GABRIEL

1. Dear Lord, I've tried to make this day A day of ser-vice true;
2. Of self - ish heart and stub-born will, I some - times lose con - trol;
3. I know I've stumbled o'er the path Thou hast ap-point-ed me,

Nor have I fol-lowed my own way, But tried Thy will to do.
But Thou art kind and pa - tient still—Blest lov - er of my soul.
But bless - ed Lord, with hold Thy wrath, Ac - cept my fer - vent plea,

Thy life has been my con-stant guide, The more like Thee to live;
I know Thou'rt ev - er near to bless, On Thee I do be - lieve!
These foes of mine Thy - self as-sailed A - gain, and yet a - gain;

But where I've failed or turned a-side, Wilt Thou, O Lord, for - give.
Yet where I've failed, and do con-fess, Wilt Thou, O Lord, for - give.
I know in man - y things I've failed, Wilt Thou, O Lord, for - give.

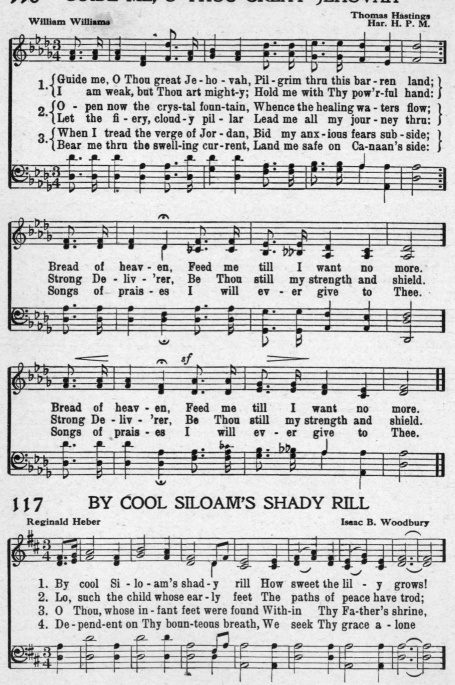

116 GUIDE ME, O THOU GREAT JEHOVAH

William Williams

Thomas Hastings
Har. H. P. M.

1. { Guide me, O Thou great Je-ho-vah, Pil-grim thru this bar-ren land;
     I am weak, but Thou art might-y; Hold me with Thy pow'r-ful hand: }

2. { O - pen now the crys-tal foun-tain, Whence the healing wa-ters flow;
     Let the fi-er-y, cloud-y pil-lar Lead me all my jour-ney thru: }

3. { When I tread the verge of Jor-dan, Bid my anx-ious fears sub-side;
     Bear me thru the swell-ing cur-rent, Land me safe on Ca-naan's side: }

Bread of heav-en, Feed me till I want no more.
Strong De-liv-'rer, Be Thou still my strength and shield.
Songs of prais-es I will ev-er give to Thee.

_sf_

Bread of heav-en, Feed me till I want no more.
Strong De-liv-'rer, Be Thou still my strength and shield.
Songs of prais-es I will ev-er give to Thee.

117 BY COOL SILOAM'S SHADY RILL

Reginald Heber

Isaac B. Woodbury

1. By cool Si-lo-am's shad-y rill How sweet the lil-y grows!
2. Lo, such the child whose ear-ly feet The paths of peace have trod;
3. O Thou, whose in-fant feet were found With-in Thy Fa-ther's shrine,
4. De-pend-ent on Thy boun-teous breath, We seek Thy grace a-lone

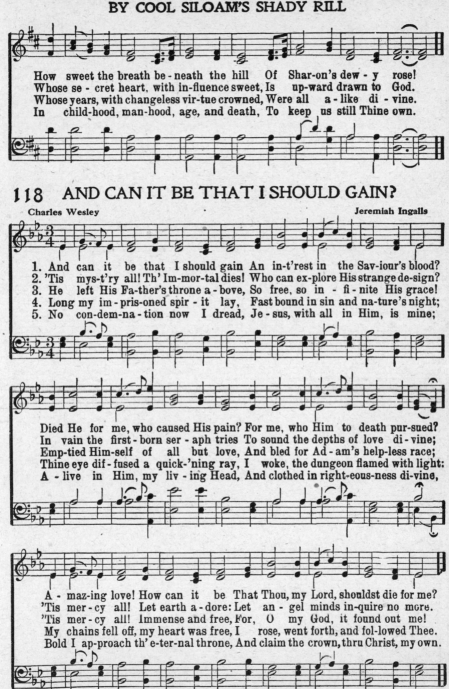

How sweet the breath be-neath the hill Of Shar-on's dew-y rose!
Whose se-cret heart, with in-fluence sweet, Is up-ward drawn to God.
Whose years, with changeless vir-tue crowned, Were all a-like di-vine.
In child-hood, man-hood, age, and death, To keep us still Thine own.

118 AND CAN IT BE THAT I SHOULD GAIN?

Charles Wesley

Jeremiah Ingalls

1. And can it be that I should gain An in-t'rest in the Sav-iour's blood?
2. 'Tis mys-t'ry all! Th' Im-mor-tal dies! Who can ex-plore His strange de-sign?
3. He left His Fa-ther's throne a-bove, So free, so in-fi-nite His grace!
4. Long my im-pris-oned spir-it lay, Fast bound in sin and na-ture's night;
5. No con-dem-na-tion now I dread, Je-sus, with all in Him, is mine;

Died He for me, who caused His pain? For me, who Him to death pur-sued?
In vain the first-born ser-aph tries To sound the depths of love di-vine;
Emp-tied Him-self of all but love, And bled for Ad-am's help-less race;
Thine eye dif-fused a quick-'ning ray, I woke, the dungeon flamed with light:
A-live in Him, my liv-ing Head, And clothed in right-eous-ness di-vine,

A-maz-ing love! How can it be That Thou, my Lord, shouldst die for me?
'Tis mer-cy all! Let earth a-dore: Let an-gel minds in-quire no more.
'Tis mer-cy all! Immense and free, For, O my God, it found out me!
My chains fell off, my heart was free, I rose, went forth, and fol-lowed Thee.
Bold I ap-proach th' e-ter-nal throne, And claim the crown, thru Christ, my own.

119 ALL HAIL THE POWER OF JESUS' NAME

EDWARD PERRONET

OLIVER HOLDEN

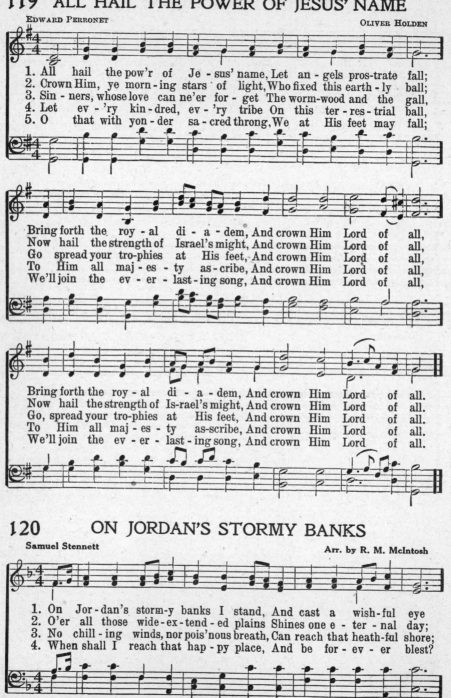

1. All hail the pow'r of Je - sus' name, Let an - gels pros-trate fall;
2. Crown Him, ye morn-ing stars of light, Who fixed this earth-ly ball;
3. Sin - ners, whose love can ne'er for - get The worm-wood and the gall,
4. Let ev - 'ry kin - dred, ev - 'ry tribe On this ter - res-trial ball,
5. O that with yon - der sa - cred throng, We at His feet may fall;

Bring forth the roy - al di - a - dem, And crown Him Lord of all,
Now hail the strength of Israel's might, And crown Him Lord of all,
Go spread your tro-phies at His feet, And crown Him Lord of all,
To Him all maj - es - ty as-cribe, And crown Him Lord of all,
We'll join the ev - er - last-ing song, And crown Him Lord of all,

Bring forth the roy - al di - a - dem, And crown Him Lord of all.
Now hail the strength of Is-rael's might, And crown Him Lord of all.
Go, spread your tro-phies at His feet, And crown Him Lord of all.
To Him all maj - es - ty as-scribe, And crown Him Lord of all.
We'll join the ev - er - last-ing song, And crown Him Lord of all.

120　　ON JORDAN'S STORMY BANKS

Samuel Stennett

Arr. by R. M. McIntosh

1. On Jor - dan's storm-y banks I stand, And cast a wish-ful eye
2. O'er all those wide - ex - tend - ed plains Shines one e - ter - nal day;
3. No chill - ing winds, nor pois'nous breath, Can reach that heath-ful shore;
4. When shall I reach that hap - py place, And be for - ev - er blest?

ON JORDAN'S STORMY BANKS

:S: FINE

To Ca-naan's fair and hap-py land, Where my pos-ses-sions lie.
There God, the Son, for-ev-er reigns, And scat-ters night a-way.
Sick-ness and sor-row, pain and death, Are felt and feared no more.
When shall I see my Fa-ther's face, And in His bos-om rest?

D.S.—*O who will come and go with me? I am bound for the prom-ised land.*

REFRAIN D.S.

I am bound for the promised land,.... I am bound for the promised land,
prom-ised land,

121 COME, THOU FOUNT

ROBERT ROBINSON JOHN WYETH
FINE

1. { Come, Thou Fount of ev-'ry bless-ing, Tune my heart to sing Thy grace; }
   { Streams of mer-cy, nev-er ceas-ing, Call for songs of loud-est praise. }
2. { Here I raise mine Eb-en-e-zer, Hith-er by Thy help I'm come; }
   { And I hope by Thy good pleasure, Safe-ly to ar-rive at home. }
3. { Oh, to grace how great a debt-or Dai-ly I'm constrained to be! }
   { Let Thy goodness, like a fet-ter, Bind my wand'ring heart to Thee: }

D.C.—*Praise the mount, I'm fixed up-on it! Mount of Thy re-deem-ing love.*
D.C.—*He, to res-cue me from dan-ger, In-ter-posed His pre-cious blood.*
D.C.—*Here's my heart, O take and seal it, Seal it for Thy courts a-bove.*

D.C.

Teach me some mel-o-dious son-net, Sung by flam-ing tongues a-bove;
Je-sus sought me when a stranger, Wand'ring from the fold of God;
Prone to wan-der, Lord, I feel it, Prone to leave the God I love;

A NEW NAME IN GLORY

C. A. M.

C. Austin Miles

1. I was once a sin-ner, but I came Par-don to re-ceive from my
2. I was humbly kneeling at the cross, Fearing naught but God's an-gry
3. In the Book 'tis written "Saved by Grace," O the joy that came to my

Lord: This was free-ly giv-en, and I found That He al-ways kept His
frown; When the heavens opened and I saw That my name was writ-ten
soul! Now I am for-giv-en and I know By the blood I am made

CHORUS

word (kept His word).
down (writ-ten down). There's a new name writ-ten down in glo-ry,
whole (am made whole).

And it's mine, O yes, it's mine! And the white-robed angels sing the
And it's mine, yes, it's mine!

sto-ry, "A sin-ner has come home." For there's a
has come home.

A NEW NAME IN GLORY

new name written down in glo-ry, And it's mine, O yes, it's mine!
And it's mine, yes, it's mine!

With my sins for-giv-en I am bound for heav-en, Nev-er-more to roam.

123   MORE ABOUT JESUS

RENEWAL COPYRIGHT, 1915, BY MRS. L. E. SWENEY
HOPE PUBLISHING CO., OWNER

E. E. Hewitt   Jno. R. Sweney

1. More a-bout Je-sus would I know, More of His grace to oth-ers show;
2. More a-bout Je-sus let me learn, More of His ho-ly will dis-cern;
3. More a-bout Je-sus; in His Word, Hold-ing com-mun-ion with my Lord;
4. More a-bout Je-sus on His throne, Rich-es in glo-ry all His own;

FINE

More of His sav-ing full-ness see, More of His love who died for me.
Spir-it of God, my teach-er be, Show-ing the things of Christ to me.
Hear-ing His voice in ev-'ry line, Mak-ing each faith-ful say-ing mine.
More of His kingdom's sure in-crease; More of His com-ing, Prince of Peace.

D. S.—*More of His sav-ing full-ness see, More of His love who died for me.*

REFRAIN   D. S.

More, more a-bout Je-sus, More, more a-bout Je-sus;

CHARLES WESLEY   JOHN ZUNDEL

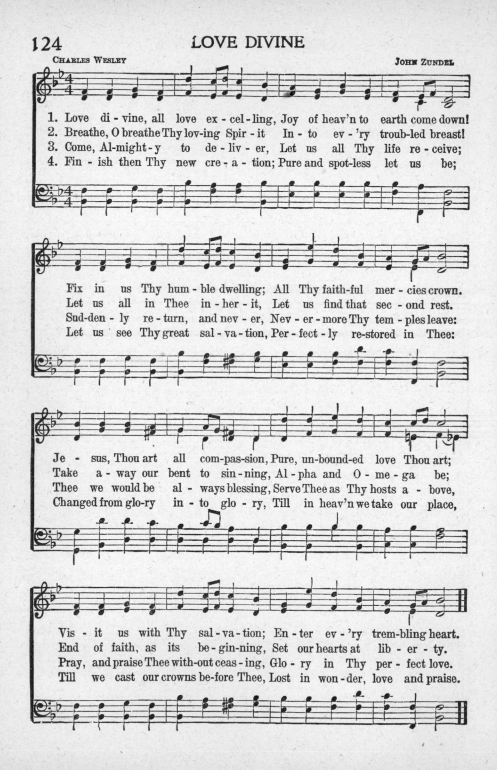

1. Love di - vine, all love ex - cel - ling, Joy of heav'n to earth come down!
2. Breathe, O breathe Thy lov-ing Spir - it In - to ev - 'ry troub-led breast!
3. Come, Al-might-y to de - liv - er, Let us all Thy life re - ceive;
4. Fin - ish then Thy new cre - a - tion; Pure and spot-less let us be;

Fix in us Thy hum - ble dwelling; All Thy faith-ful mer - cies crown.
Let us all in Thee in - her - it, Let us find that sec - ond rest.
Sud-den - ly re - turn, and nev - er, Nev - er-more Thy tem - ples leave:
Let us see Thy great sal - va - tion, Per - fect - ly re-stored in Thee:

Je - sus, Thou art all com-pas-sion, Pure, un-bound-ed love Thou art;
Take a - way our bent to sin-ning, Al - pha and O - me - ga be;
Thee we would be al - ways blessing, Serve Thee as Thy hosts a - bove,
Changed from glo-ry in - to glo - ry, Till in heav'n we take our place,

Vis - it us with Thy sal - va - tion; En - ter ev - 'ry trem-bling heart.
End of faith, as its be - gin-ning, Set our hearts at lib - er - ty.
Pray, and praise Thee with-out ceas - ing, Glo - ry in Thy per - fect love.
Till we cast our crowns be-fore Thee, Lost in won - der, love and praise.

125 SOMEBODY KNOWS

Alfred H. Ackley

B. D. Ackley

1. Fail-ing in strength when opprest by my foes, Somebody knows, Somebody knows;
2. Why should I fear when the care-bil-lows roll? Somebody knows, Somebody knows;
3. Wounded and helpless and sick with distress, Somebody knows, Somebody knows;

Wait-ing for some-one to ban-ish my woes, Some-bod-y knows,—'tis Je-sus.
When the deep shadows sweep o-ver my soul, Some-bod-y knows,—'tis Je-sus.
Long-ing for home and a mother's ca-ress, Some-bod-y knows,—'tis Je-sus.

Chorus or Quartet

Some-bod-y knows, Some-bod-y knows When I am tempted and tried by my foes;

He is the One who will keep me— Some-bod-y knows—'tis Je-sus.

126 GOOD NIGHT AND GOOD MORNING

Lizzie DeArmond   Homer A. Rodeheaver

1. When comes to the wea-ry a bless-ed re-lease, When upward we
2. When fad-eth the day and dark shadows draw nigh, With Christ close at
3. When home-lights we see shin-ing bright-ly a-bove, Where we shall be

pass to His kingdom of peace, When free from the woes that on earth we must bear,
hand, it is not death to die; He'll wipe ev-'ry tear, roll a-way ev-'ry care;
soon, thro' His wonderful love, We'll praise Him who called us His heaven to share,

CHORUS.

We'll say "good-night," here, but "good-morning" up there.
We'll say "good-night," here, but "good-morning" up there. Good morning up there where
We'll say "good-night," here, but "good-morning" up there.

Christ is the Light, Good-morning up there where cometh no night; When we step from this

earth to God's heaven so fair, We'll say "good-night" here, but "good-morning" up there.

127 SOME OF THESE DAYS

F. L. S.   J. Lincoln Hall

Duet (*Soprano and Alto*)

1. Some of these days all the skies will be bright-er— Some of these days all the
2. Some of these days, in the des-erts up-spring-ing, Fountains shall flash, while the
3. Some of these days! Let us bear with our sor-row; Faith in the fu-ture—its

bur-dens be light-er; Hearts will be hap-pi-er, souls will be whit-er—
joy-bells are ring-ing, And all the world, with the birds, shall go sing-ing,
light we may bor-row; There will be joy in the gold-en to-mor-row,

Chorus

Some of these days, some of these days! Some of these days, . . . some of these
Some of these days,

days, ... Skies will be bright-er some of these days; . . . .
some of these days,   *some of these days;*

rit.

Some of these days all the burdens be lighter, Some of these days, some of these days!

MARCHING WITH THE HEROES

William George Tarrant

Adam Geibel

Unison

1. Marching with the he - roes, Com-rades of the strong, Lift we hearts and
2. Glo - ry to the he - roes, Who in days of old Trod the path of
3. So we sing the sto - ry Of the brave and true, Till a - mong the

voic - es As we march a - long; O the joy - ful mu - sic
du - ty, Faith-ful, wise, and bold; For the right un - flinch - ing,
he - roes We are he - roes, too; Loy - al to our Cap - tain

All in cho - rus raise! Theirs the song of tri-umph, Ours the song of praise.
Strong the weak to save, War - riors all and free-men, Fighting for the slave.
Like the men of yore, March-ing with the he - roes, On-ward ev - er - more.

REFRAIN. *Harmony*

March - ing with the he - roes, Com - rades of the strong,
March-ing, march-ing

Lift we hearts and voic - es As we march a - long.

YIELD NOT TO TEMPTATION

H. R. Palmer

H. R. Palmer

1. Yield not to temp-ta-tion, For yield-ing is sin; Each vic-t'ry will
2. Shun e-vil com-pan-ions, Bad lan-guage dis-dain; God's name hold in
3. To him that o'er-com-eth, God giv-eth a crown; Thro' faith we will

help you Some oth-er to win; Fight man-ful-ly on-ward,
rev-'rence, Nor take it in vain; Be thought-ful and ear-nest,
con-quer, Tho' oft-en cast down; He who is our Sav-iour,

Dark pas-sions sub-due; Look ev-er to Je-sus, He'll car-ry you through.
Kind-heart-ed and true; Look ev-er to Je-sus, He'll car-ry you through.
Our strength will re-new; Look ev-er to Je-sus, He'll car-ry you through.

REFRAIN

Ask the Sav-iour to help you, Com-fort, strength-en, and keep you;

He is will-ing to aid you, He will car-ry you through.

ROCK OF AGES

130

Augustus M. Toplady

Thomas Hastings

1. Rock of A - ges, cleft for me, Let me hide my - self in Thee;
2. Could my tears for - ev - er flow, Could my zeal no lan-guor know,
3. While I draw this fleet - ing breath, When my eyes shall close in death,

Let the wa - ter and the blood, From Thy wound - ed side which flowed,
These for sin could not a - tone; Thou must save, and Thou a - lone:
When I rise to worlds unknown, And be - hold Thee on Thy throne,

Be of sin the dou - ble cure, Save from wrath and make me pure.
In my hand no price I bring, Sim - ply to Thy cross I cling.
Rock of A - ges, cleft for me, Let me hide my - self in Thee.

NEARER, MY GOD, TO THEE

131

Sarah F. Adams

Arr. by Lowell Mason

1. Near - er, my God, to Thee, Near - er to Thee! E'en though it
2. Though like the wan - der - er, The sun gone down, Dark - ness be
3. There let the way ap-pear, Steps un - to heav'n: All that Thou
4. Then, with my wak - ing tho'ts Bright with Thy praise, Out of my
5. Or if on joy - ful wing, Cleav - ing the sky, Sun, moon, and

NEARER, MY GOD, TO THEE

be a cross	That rais - eth	me;	Still all	my song shall be,
o - ver me,	My rest a	stone;	Yet in	my dreams I'd be
send - est me,	In mer - cy	giv'n:	An - gels	to beck - on me,
sto - ny griefs	Beth - el I'll	raise;	So by	my woes to be
stars for - got,	Up - wards I'll	fly,	Still all	my song shall be,

Near - er, my God, to Thee, Near - er, my God, to Thee, Nearer, to Thee!

132 JESUS, LOVER OF MY SOUL

CHARLES WESLEY

S. B. MARSH
FINE

1. { Je - sus, Lov - er of my soul, Let me to Thy bos - om fly, }
   { While the near - er wa - ters roll, While the tem-pest still is high! }
2. { Oth - er ref - uge have I none; Hangs my help-less soul on Thee: }
   { Leave, ah, leave me not a - lone, Still sup-port and com-fort me! }
3. { Thou, O Christ, art all I want; More than all in Thee I find; }
   { Raise the fall - en, cheer the faint, Heal the sick, and lead the blind. }
4. { Plenteous grace with Thee is found, Grace to cov - er all my sin; }
   { Let the heal - ing streams abound, Make and keep me pure with - in. }

D. C.—*Safe in - to the ha - ven guide, O re - ceive my soul at last!*
D. C.—*Cov - er my de - fense - less head With the shad - ow of Thy wing.*
D. C.—*False and full of sin I am, Thou art full of truth and grace.*
D. C.—*Spring Thou up with - in my heart, Rise to all e - ter - ni - ty.*

D. C.

Hide me, O my Sav - ior, hide, Till the storm of life is past;
All my trust on Thee is stayed, All my help from Thee I bring;
Just and ho - ly is Thy name, I am all un-right-eous-ness;
Thou of life the foun-tain art; Free - ly let me take of Thee;

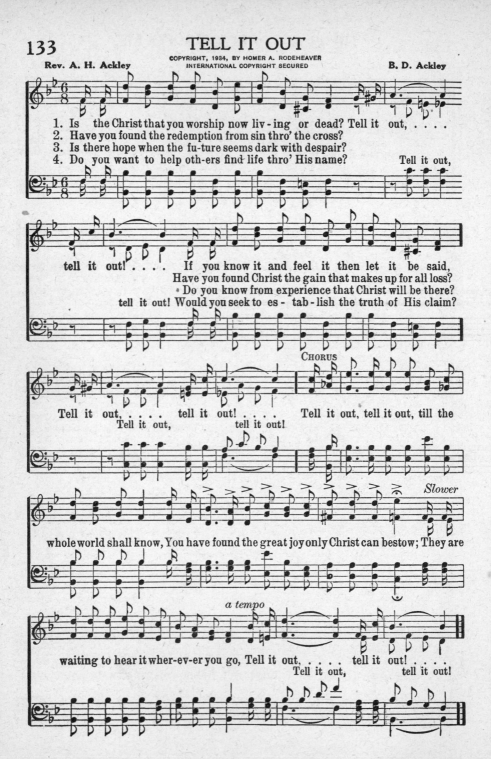

133 TELL IT OUT

Rev. A. H. Ackley

B. D. Ackley

1. Is the Christ that you worship now liv-ing or dead? Tell it out, ...
2. Have you found the redemption from sin thro' the cross?
3. Is there hope when the fu-ture seems dark with despair?
4. Do you want to help oth-ers find life thro' His name?

Tell it out,

tell it out! .... If you know it and feel it then let it be said,
Have you found Christ the gain that makes up for all loss?
Do you know from experience that Christ will be there?
tell it out! Would you seek to es-tab-lish the truth of His claim?

CHORUS

Tell it out, ... tell it out! .... Tell it out, tell it out, till the
Tell it out, tell it out!

Slower

whole world shall know, You have found the great joy only Christ can bestow; They are

a tempo

waiting to hear it wher-ev-er you go, Tell it out, ... tell it out! ....
Tell it out, tell it out!

134 HE IS SO PRECIOUS TO ME

C. H. G.

COPYRIGHT, 1930, RENEWAL
HOMER A. RODEHEAVER, OWNER

Chas. H. Gabriel

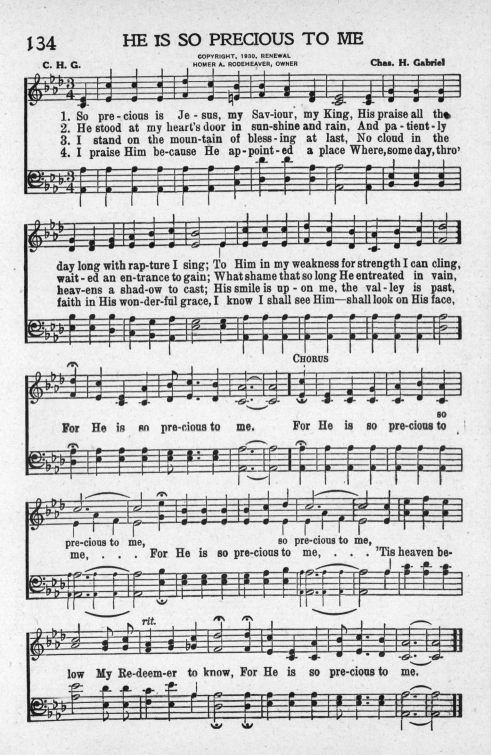

1. So pre-cious is Je-sus, my Sav-iour, my King, His praise all the
2. He stood at my heart's door in sun-shine and rain, And pa-tient-ly
3. I stand on the moun-tain of bless-ing at last, No cloud in the
4. I praise Him be-cause He ap-point-ed a place Where, some day, thro'

day long with rap-ture I sing; To Him in my weakness for strength I can cling,
wait-ed an en-trance to gain; What shame that so long He entreated in vain,
heav-ens a shad-ow to cast; His smile is up-on me, the val-ley is past,
faith in His won-der-ful grace, I know I shall see Him—shall look on His face,

CHORUS

For He is so pre-cious to me. For He is so pre-cious to

pre-cious to me, so pre-cious to me,
me, . . . For He is so pre-cious to me, . . . 'Tis heaven be-

rit.

low My Re-deem-er to know, For He is so pre-cious to me.

135 GOD UNDERSTANDS

Oswald J. Smith

B. D. Ackley

Slowly, with expression

1. God un-der-stands your sor-row, He sees the fall-ing tear,
2. God un-der-stands your heart-ache, He knows the bit-ter pain;
3. God un-der-stands your weak-ness, He knows the tempt-er's pow'r;

And whis-pers, "I am with thee," Then fal-ter not, nor fear.
O, trust Him in the dark-ness, You can-not trust in vain.
And He will walk be-side you How-ev-er dark the hour.

REFRAIN

He un-der-stands your long-ing, Your deep-est grief He shares;

Then let Him bear your bur-den, He un-der-stands, and cares.

136 TRUST AND OBEY

J. H. SAMMIS

D. B. TOWNER

1. When we walk with the Lord In the light of His Word What a glo-ry He
2. Not a shad-ow can rise, Not a cloud in the skies, But His smile quickly
3. Not a bur-den we bear, Not a sor-row we share, But our toil He doth
4. But we nev-er can prove The de-lights of His love Un-til all on the
5. Then in fel-low-ship sweet We will sit at His feet, Or we'll walk by His

sheds on our way! While we do His good will, He a-bides with us still,
drives it a-way; Not a doubt nor a fear, Not a sigh nor a tear,
rich-ly re-pay; Not a grief nor a loss, Not a frown nor a cross,
al-tar we lay; For the fa-vor He shows, And the joy He be-stows,
side in the way; What He says we will do, Where He sends we will go,—

CHORUS

And with all who will trust and o-bey.
Can a-bide while we trust and o-bey.
But is blest if we trust and o-bey.
Are for them who will trust and o-bey.
Nev-er fear, on-ly trust and o-bey.

Trust and o-bey, for there's no oth-er

way To be hap-py in Je-sus, but to trust and o-bey.

137 O MASTER, LET ME WALK WITH THEE

Washington Gladden — CANONBURY L. M. — Robert Schumann

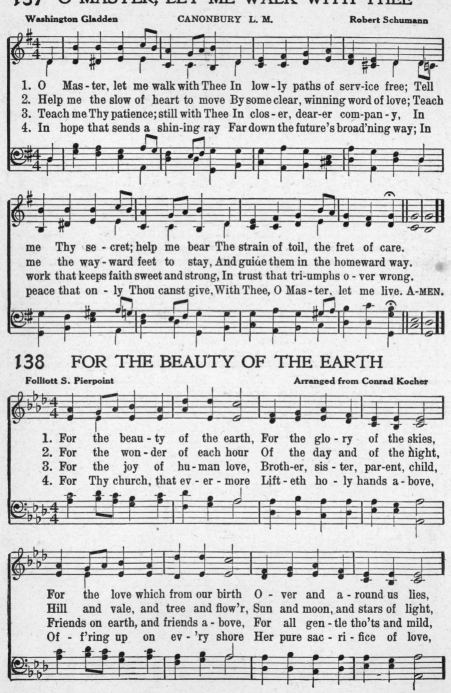

1. O Mas-ter, let me walk with Thee In low-ly paths of serv-ice free; Tell
2. Help me the slow of heart to move By some clear, winning word of love; Teach
3. Teach me Thy patience; still with Thee In clos-er, dear-er com-pan-y, In
4. In hope that sends a shin-ing ray Far down the future's broad'ning way; In

me Thy se-cret; help me bear The strain of toil, the fret of care.
me the way-ward feet to stay, And guide them in the homeward way.
work that keeps faith sweet and strong, In trust that tri-umphs o-ver wrong.
peace that on-ly Thou canst give, With Thee, O Mas-ter, let me live. A-MEN.

138 FOR THE BEAUTY OF THE EARTH

Folliott S. Pierpoint — Arranged from Conrad Kocher

1. For the beau-ty of the earth, For the glo-ry of the skies,
2. For the won-der of each hour Of the day and of the night,
3. For the joy of hu-man love, Broth-er, sis-ter, par-ent, child,
4. For Thy church, that ev-er-more Lift-eth ho-ly hands a-bove,

For the love which from our birth O-ver and a-round us lies,
Hill and vale, and tree and flow'r, Sun and moon, and stars of light,
Friends on earth, and friends a-bove, For all gen-tle tho'ts and mild,
Of-f'ring up on ev-'ry shore Her pure sac-ri-fice of love,

FOR THE BEAUTY OF THE EARTH

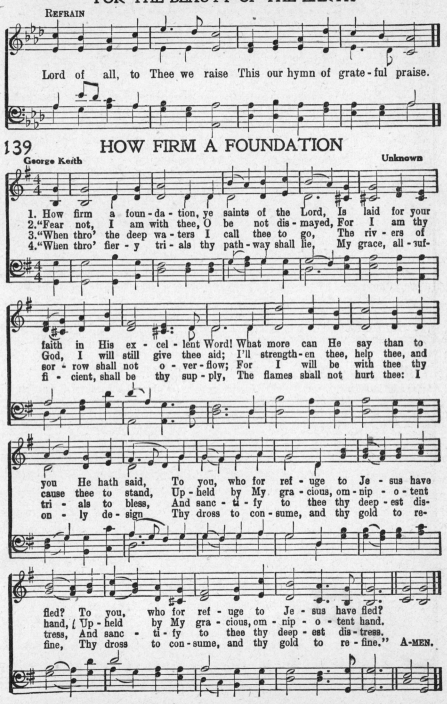

REFRAIN

Lord of all, to Thee we raise This our hymn of grate-ful praise.

139   HOW FIRM A FOUNDATION

George Keith

Unknown

1. How firm a foun-da-tion, ye saints of the Lord, Is laid for your
2. "Fear not, I am with thee, O be not dis-mayed, For I am thy
3. "When thro' the deep wa-ters I call thee to go, The riv-ers of
4. "When thro' fier-y tri-als thy path-way shall lie, My grace, all-suf-

faith in His ex-cel-lent Word! What more can He say than to
God, I will still give thee aid; I'll strength-en thee, help thee, and
sor-row shall not o-ver-flow; For I will be with thee thy
fi-cient, shall be thy sup-ply, The flames shall not hurt thee: I

you He hath said, To you, who for ref-uge to Je-sus have
cause thee to stand, Up-held by My gra-cious, om-nip-o-tent
tri-als to bless, And sanc-ti-fy to thee thy deep-est dis-
on-ly de-sign Thy dross to con-sume, and thy gold to re-

fled? To you, who for ref-uge to Je-sus have fled?
hand, Up-held by My gra-cious, om-nip-o-tent hand.
tress, And sanc-ti-fy to thee thy deep-est dis-tress.
fine, Thy dross to con-sume, and thy gold to re-fine." A-MEN.

140 ONE DAY

Dr. J. Wilbur Chapman

Chas. H. Marsh

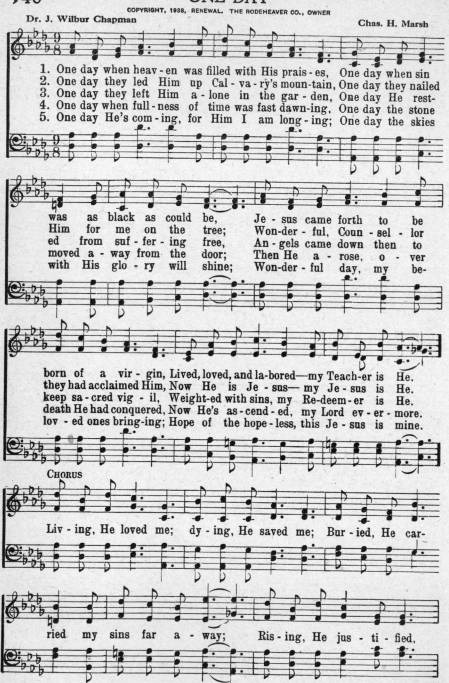

1. One day when heav-en was filled with His prais-es, One day when sin
2. One day they led Him up Cal-va-ry's moun-tain, One day they nailed
3. One day they left Him a-lone in the gar-den, One day He rest-
4. One day when full-ness of time was fast dawn-ing, One day the stone
5. One day He's com-ing, for Him I am long-ing; One day the skies

was as black as could be, Je-sus came forth to be
Him for me on the tree; Won-der-ful, Coun-sel-lor
ed from suf-fer-ing free, An-gels came down then to
moved a-way from the door; Then He a-rose, o-ver
with His glo-ry will shine; Won-der-ful day, my be-

born of a vir-gin, Lived, loved, and la-bored—my Teach-er is He.
they had acclaimed Him, Now He is Je-sus— my Je-sus is He.
keep sa-cred vig-il, Weight-ed with sins, my Re-deem-er is He.
death He had conquered, Now He's as-cend-ed, my Lord ev-er-more.
lov-ed ones bring-ing; Hope of the hope-less, this Je-sus is mine.

CHORUS

Liv-ing, He loved me; dy-ing, He saved me; Bur-ied, He car-

ried my sins far a-way; Ris-ing, He jus-ti-fied,

ONE DAY

free - ly for - ev - er: One day He's com - ing—O glo - ri - ous day!

141 THE INNER CIRCLE

Flora Kirkland

W. S. Weeden

1. Have you heard the voice of Je - sus Whis-per, "I have cho - sen you?"
2. As the first dis - ci - ples fol - lowed, As they went wher-e'er He sent;
3. Or, if He shall choose to send us On some er - rand in His name,
4. Mas - ter, at Thy foot-stool kneel-ing, We, Thy chil - dren, hum-bly wait;

Does He tell you in com-mun - ion What He wish - es you to do?
So to - day we, too, may fol - low, On His lead - ing still in - tent.
We can serve Him as dis - ci - ples, For our place is just the same.
Lead us, send us, bless us, use us, Till we en - ter heav-en's gate.

CHORUS

Are you in the in - ner cir - cle? Have you heard the Mas-ter's call?
Are you in the in - ner cir - cle? Have you heard the Master's call?

Have you giv'n your life to Je - sus? Is He now your All in all?
Have you giv'n your life to Je - sus?

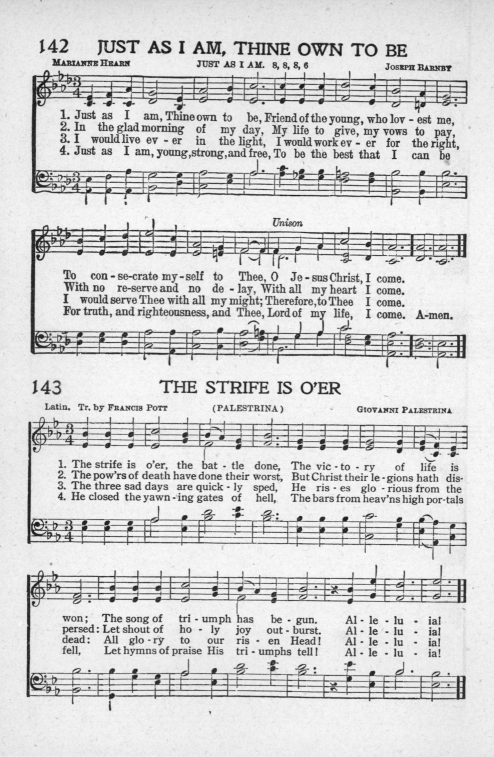

142 JUST AS I AM, THINE OWN TO BE

MARIANNE HEARN   JUST AS I AM. 8, 8, 8, 6   JOSEPH BARNBY

1. Just as I am, Thine own to be, Friend of the young, who lov - est me,
2. In the glad morning of my day, My life to give, my vows to pay,
4. Just as I am, young, strong, and free, To be the best that I can be

Unison

To con - se - crate my - self to Thee, O Je - sus Christ, I come.
With no re - serve and no de - lay, With all my heart I come.
I would serve Thee with all my might; Therefore, to Thee I come.
For truth, and righteousness, and Thee, Lord of my life, I come. A-men.

143 THE STRIFE IS O'ER

Latin. Tr. by FRANCIS POTT   (PALESTRINA)   GIOVANNI PALESTRINA

1. The strife is o'er, the bat - tle done, The vic - to - ry of life is
2. The pow'rs of death have done their worst, But Christ their le - gions hath dis -
3. The three sad days are quick - ly sped, He ris - es glo - rious from the
4. He closed the yawn - ing gates of hell, The bars from heav'ns high por - tals

won; The song of tri - umph has be - gun. Al - le - lu - ia!
persed: Let shout of ho - ly joy out - burst. Al - le - lu - ia!
dead: All glo - ry to our ris - en Head! Al - le - lu - ia!
fell, Let hymns of praise His tri - umphs tell! Al - le - lu - ia!

144 MAJESTIC SWEETNESS SITS ENTHRONED

Samuel Stennett   ORTONVILLE C. M.   Thomas Hastings

1. Majestic sweetness sits enthroned Upon the Saviour's brow; His head with radiant
2. He saw me plunged in deep distress, He flew to my relief; For me He bore the
3. To Him I owe my life and breath, And all the joys I have; He makes me triumph
4. To heav'n, the place of His abode, He brings my weary feet; Shows me the glories
5. Since from His bounty I receive Such proofs of love divine, Had I a thousand

glories crowned, His lips with grace o'erflow, His lips with grace o'erflow.
shameful cross, And carried all my grief, And carried all my grief.
o - ver death, He saves me from the grave, He saves me from the grave.
of my God, And makes my joys complete, And makes my joys complete.
hearts to give, Lord, they should all be Thine, Lord, they should all be Thine. A - men.

145 WE MAY NOT CLIMB THE HEAVENLY STEEPS

John G. Whittier   SERENITY C. M.   William V. Wallace

1. We may not climb the heav'n-ly steeps To bring the Lord Christ down;
2. But warm, sweet, ten-der e - ven yet A pres - ent help is He;
3. The heal - ing of His seam - less dress Is by our beds of pain;
4. Thro' Him the first fond pray'rs are said Our lips of child-hood frame;
5. O Lord and Mas-ter of us all, What-e'er our name or sign,

In vain we search the low - est deeps, For Him no depths can drown.
And faith has still its Ol - i - vet, And love its Gal - i - lee.
We touch Him in life's throng and press, And we are whole a-gain.
The last low whispers of our dead Are burdened with His name.
We own Thy sway, we hear Thy call, We test our lives by Thine! A - men.

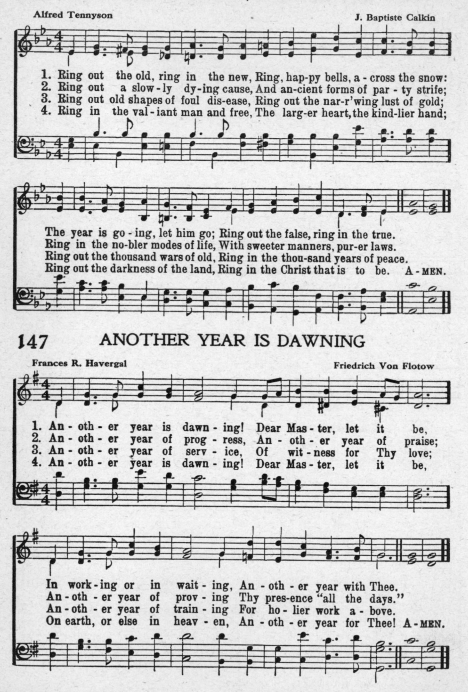

146 RING OUT THE OLD, RING IN THE NEW

Alfred Tennyson   J. Baptiste Calkin

1. Ring out the old, ring in the new, Ring, hap-py bells, a-cross the snow:
2. Ring out a slow-ly dy-ing cause, And an-cient forms of par-ty strife;
3. Ring out old shapes of foul dis-ease, Ring out the nar-r'wing lust of gold;
4. Ring in the val-iant man and free, The larg-er heart, the kind-lier hand;

The year is go-ing, let him go; Ring out the false, ring in the true.
Ring in the no-bler modes of life, With sweeter manners, pur-er laws.
Ring out the thousand wars of old, Ring in the thou-sand years of peace.
Ring out the darkness of the land, Ring in the Christ that is to be. A-MEN.

147 ANOTHER YEAR IS DAWNING

Frances R. Havergal   Friedrich Von Flotow

1. An-oth-er year is dawn-ing! Dear Mas-ter, let it be,
2. An-oth-er year of prog-ress, An-oth-er year of praise;
3. An-oth-er year of serv-ice, Of wit-ness for Thy love;
4. An-oth-er year is dawn-ing! Dear Mas-ter, let it be,

In work-ing or in wait-ing, An-oth-er year with Thee.
An-oth-er year of prov-ing Thy pres-ence "all the days."
An-oth-er year of train-ing For ho-lier work a-bove.
On earth, or else in heav-en, An-oth-er year for Thee! A-MEN.

CLOSE TO HIS SIDE

REV. A. H. ACKLEY   B. D. ACKLEY

1. I've found a ref-uge where none can mo-lest, Close, close to His
2. Full-est pro-tec-tion I find from all harm, Close, close to His
3. Heav-en-ly treas-ure is my rich-est gain, Close, close to His
4. There will I stay till I come to the goal, Close, close to His

side,............... Where in my weak-ness with strength I am blest,
side,............... Peace and con-tent-ment when foes would a-larm,
side,............... Glo-ry e-ter-nal if I but re-main,
side,............... Je-sus for-ev-er will shel-ter my soul,

to His side,

CHORUS

Close, close to His side. Close, close to His side,...............
to His side,

Close, close to His side;............... Je-sus will hide me,
to His side,

com-fort and guide me, Close, close to His side.

149 I'LL LIVE FOR HIM

R. E. Hudson

C. R. Dunbar

1. My life, my love, I give to Thee, Thou Lamb of God who died for me;
2. I now be-lieve Thou dost re-ceive, For Thou hast died that I might live;
3. O Thou who died on Cal-va-ry, To save my soul and make me free,

CHO.—*I'll live for Him who died for me, How hap-py then my life shall be!*

D. C. Chorus

Oh, may I ev - er faith-ful be, My Sav-iour and my God!
And now hence-forth I'll trust in Thee, My Sav-iour and my God!
I'll con - se-crate my life to Thee, My Sav-iour and my God!

I'll live for Him who died for me, My Sav-iour and my God!

150 I SURRENDER ALL

J. W. Van Deventer

W. S. Weeden

1. All to Je - sus I sur - ren - der, All to Him I free - ly give;
2. All to Je - sus I sur - ren - der, Hum-bly at His feet I bow,
3. All to Je - sus I sur - ren - der, Make me, Sav-ior, whol - ly Thine;
4. All to Je - sus I sur - ren - der, Lord, I give my - self to Thee;
5. All to Je - sus I sur - ren - der, Now I feel the sa - cred flame;

I will ev - er love and trust Him, In His pres-ence dai - ly live.
World-ly pleas-ures all for-sak - en, Take me, Je - sus, take me now.
Let me feel the Ho - ly Spir - it,—Tru - ly know that Thou art mine.
Fill me with Thy love and pow - er, Let Thy bless-ing fall on me.
Oh, the joy of full sal - va - tion! Glo - ry, glo - ry to His name!

I SURRENDER ALL

Chorus

I sur-ren-der all, I sur-ren-der all,

I sur-ren-der all, I sur-ren-der all,

All to Thee, my bless-ed Sav-ior, I sur-ren-der all.

151   MY PRAYER

COPYRIGHT, 1936, BY THE RODEHEAVER CO.
INTERNATIONAL COPYRIGHT SECURED

E. A.   Mrs. Edw. Augsburger

1. Lord, make my life to-day A life of prayer, That I may in-ter-cede
2. Lord, make me more like Thee, Be Thou my Guide; O, fill my life with love,

For souls ev-'ry-where. Lord, give me a bur-den to-day For the lost on life's
In Thee to a-bide. Lord, grant my de-sire to-day, That my life may bring

per-il-ous sea; Help me to guide them safely to Thee, Lord, help me, I pray.
glo-ry to Thee; Saving souls from life's treacherous sea, Lord, help me, I pray.

152 HE LIVES

A. H. A.

Rev. A. H. Ackley

1. I serve a ris-en Sav-iour, He's in the world to-day; I know that He is liv-ing, what-ev-er men may say; I see His hand of mer-cy, I hear His voice of cheer, And just the time I need Him He's al-ways near.

2. In all the world a-round me I see His lov-ing care, And tho' my heart grows wea-ry I nev-er will de-spair; I know that He is lead-ing, thro' all the storm-y blast, The day of His ap-pear-ing will come at last.

3. Re-joice, re-joice, O Christian, lift up your voice and sing E-ter-nal hal-le-lu-jahs to Je-sus Christ the King! The Hope of all who seek Him, the Help of all who find, None oth-er is so lov-ing, so good and kind.

REFRAIN *Spirited*

He lives, He lives, Christ Je-sus lives to-day! He walks with me and talks with me a-long life's nar-row way. He lives, He lives, sal-

rit. ff

va-tion to im - part! You ask me how I know He lives? He lives within my heart.

153

GOD OF OUR FATHERS

Daniel C. Roberts,

George W. Warren,

Trumpets, before each verse.

1. God of our fa-thers, whose al-might-y hand
2. Thy love di - vine hath led us in the past,
3. From war's a-larms, from dead-ly pes - ti-lence,
4. Re - fresh Thy peo - ple on their toil-some way,

Leads forth in beau - ty all the star-ry band   Of shin - ing worlds in
In   this free land by Thee our lot is cast;   Be Thou our Rul - er,
Be   Thy strong arm our ev - er sure de-fense;   Thy true re - lig - ion
Lead   us from night to nev-er-end-ing day;   Fill all our lives with

splen-dor thru the skies,   Our grate-ful songs be-fore Thy throne a - rise.
Guardian, Guide and Stay,   Thy word our law, Thy paths our cho-sen way.
in our hearts in-crease,   Thy bounteous goodness nourish us in peace.
love and grace di - vine,   And glo - ry, laud and praise be ev - er Thine.

154 LORD, SPEAK TO ME, THAT I MAY SPEAK

Frances R. Havergal   CANONBURY L. M.   Robert A. Schumann

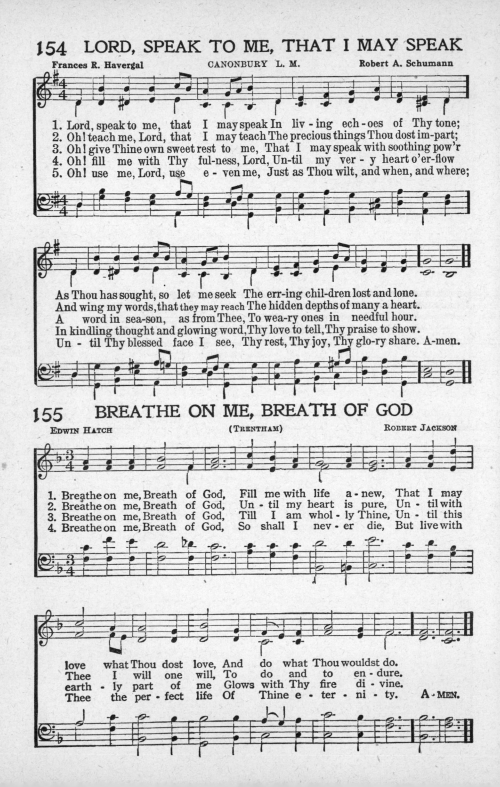

1. Lord, speak to me, that I may speak In liv-ing ech-oes of Thy tone;
2. Oh! teach me, Lord, that I may teach The precious things Thou dost im-part;
3. Oh! give Thine own sweet rest to me, That I may speak with soothing pow'r
4. Oh! fill me with Thy ful-ness, Lord, Un-til my ver-y heart o'er-flow
5. Oh! use me, Lord, use e-ven me, Just as Thou wilt, and when, and where;

As Thou has sought, so let me seek The err-ing chil-dren lost and lone.
And wing my words, that they may reach The hidden depths of many a heart.
A word in sea-son, as from Thee, To wea-ry ones in needful hour.
In kindling thought and glowing word, Thy love to tell, Thy praise to show.
Un-til Thy blessed face I see, Thy rest, Thy joy, Thy glo-ry share. A-men.

155 BREATHE ON ME, BREATH OF GOD

Edwin Hatch   (Trentham)   Robert Jackson

1. Breathe on me, Breath of God, Fill me with life a-new, That I may
2. Breathe on me, Breath of God, Un-til my heart is pure, Un-til with
3. Breathe on me, Breath of God, Till I am whol-ly Thine, Un-til this
4. Breathe on me, Breath of God, So shall I nev-er die, But live with

love what Thou dost love, And do what Thou wouldst do.
Thee I will one will, To do and to en-dure.
earth-ly part of me Glows with Thy fire di-vine.
Thee the per-fect life Of Thine e-ter-ni-ty. A-men.

156 PRAYER IS THE SOUL'S SINCERE DESIRE

James Montgomery   LAMBETH C. M.   Anonymous

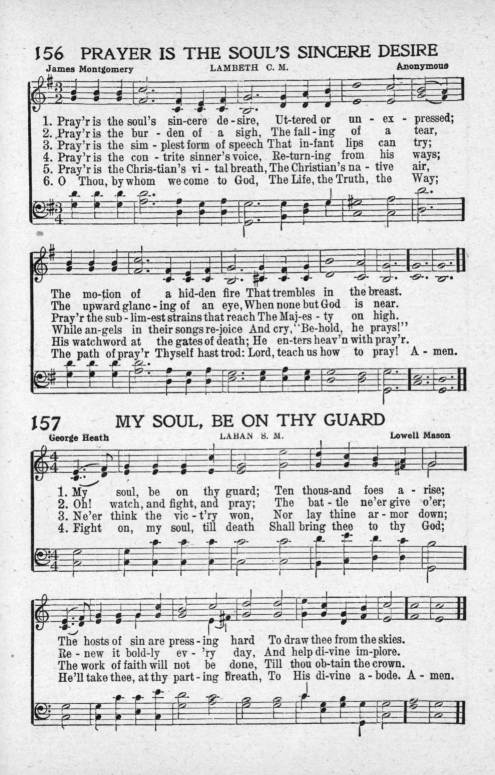

1. Pray'r is the soul's sin-cere de-sire, Ut-tered or un - ex - pressed;
2. Pray'r is the bur - den of a sigh, The fall-ing of a tear,
3. Pray'r is the sim - plest form of speech That in-fant lips can try;
4. Pray'r is the con - trite sinner's voice, Re-turn-ing from his ways;
5. Pray'r is the Chris-tian's vi - tal breath, The Christian's na - tive air,
6. O Thou, by whom we come to God, The Life, the Truth, the Way;

The mo-tion of a hid-den fire That trembles in the breast.
The upward glanc-ing of an eye, When none but God is near.
Pray'r the sub - lim-est strains that reach The Maj-es - ty on high.
While an-gels in their songs re-joice And cry, "Be-hold, he prays!"
His watchword at the gates of death; He en-ters heav'n with pray'r.
The path of pray'r Thyself hast trod: Lord, teach us how to pray! A - men.

157 MY SOUL, BE ON THY GUARD

George Heath   LABAN S. M.   Lowell Mason

1. My soul, be on thy guard; Ten thous-and foes a - rise;
2. Oh! watch, and fight, and pray; The bat - tle ne'er give o'er;
3. Ne'er think the vic - t'ry won, Nor lay thine ar - mor down;
4. Fight on, my soul, till death Shall bring thee to thy God;

The hosts of sin are press-ing hard To draw thee from the skies.
Re - new it bold-ly ev'ry day, And help di-vine im-plore.
The work of faith will not be done, Till thou ob-tain the crown.
He'll take thee, at thy part-ing breath, To His di-vine a - bode. A - men.

158 LIVING FOR JESUS

T. O. CHISHOLM

C. HAROLD LOWDEN

Not fast

1. Liv-ing for Je-sus a life that is true, Striving to please Him in all that I do,
2. Liv-ing for Je-sus who died in my place, Bearing on Calv'ry my sin and disgrace,
3. Liv-ing for Je-sus wher-ev-er I am, Do-ing each du-ty in His Ho-ly Name,
4. Living for Jesus thro' earth's little while, My dearest treasure, the light of His smile,

Yielding allegiance, glad-hearted and free, This is the pathway of blessing for me.
Such love constrains me to answer His call, Follow His leading and give Him my all.
Will-ing to suf-fer af-flic-tion or loss, Deeming each trial a part of my cross.
Seek-ing the lost ones He died to redeem, Bringing the weary to find rest in Him.

* CHORUS. UNISON. *A little slower.*

O Je-sus, Lord and Savior, I give my-self to Thee; For Thou, in Thy a-

tonement, Didst give Thyself for me; I own no oth-er Mas-ter, My

rit.............

heart shall be Thy throne, My life I give, henceforth to live, O Christ, for Thee alone.

*Melody in lower notes. A two-part effect may be had by having the men sing the melody, the women taking the middle notes.

159 JESUS, ROSE OF SHARON

Ida A. Guirey   Chas. H. Gabriel

1. Je - sus, Rose of Shar - on, bloom with - in my heart; Beau - ties of Thy
2. Je - sus, Rose of Shar - on, sweet - er far to me Than the fair - est
3. Je - sus, Rose of Shar - on, balm for ev - 'ry ill, May Thy ten - der
4. Je - sus, Rose of Shar - on, bloom for - ev - er - more; Be Thy glo - ry

truth and ho - li - ness im - part, That wher-e'er I go my life may
flow'rs of earth could ev - er be, Fill my life com-plete - ly, add - ing
mer - cy's healing pow'r dis - til For af - flic - ted souls of wea - ry,
seen on earth from shore to shore, Till the na-tions own Thy Sov'-reign-

shed a-broad Fra-grance of the knowledge of the love of God.
more each day Of Thy grace di - vine and pur - i - ty, I pray.
bur-dened men, Giv - ing need - y mor-tals health and hope a - gain.
ty complete, Lay their hon - ors down and worship at Thy feet.

REFRAIN.

Je - sus,   Rose of Shar - on, ...
Bless - ed Je - sus,   Rose of Shar - on,

Bloom in ra - diance and in love with - in my heart.

160 DWELLING IN BEULAH LAND

C. A. M.

C. AUSTIN MILES

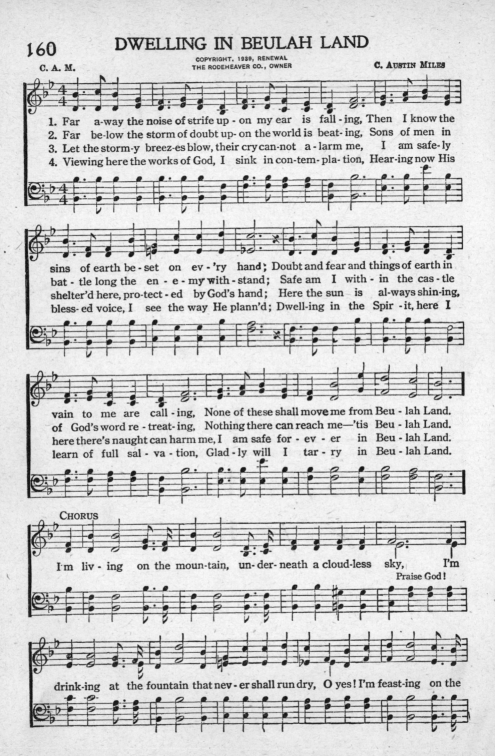

1. Far a-way the noise of strife up-on my ear is fall-ing, Then I know the
2. Far be-low the storm of doubt up-on the world is beat-ing, Sons of men in
3. Let the storm-y breez-es blow, their cry can-not a-larm me, I am safe-ly
4. Viewing here the works of God, I sink in con-tem-pla-tion, Hear-ing now His

sins of earth be-set on ev-'ry hand; Doubt and fear and things of earth in
bat-tle long the en-e-my with-stand; Safe am I with-in the cas-tle
shelter'd here, pro-tect-ed by God's hand; Here the sun is al-ways shin-ing,
bless-ed voice, I see the way He plann'd; Dwell-ing in the Spir-it, here I

vain to me are call-ing, None of these shall move me from Beu-lah Land.
of God's word re-treat-ing, Nothing there can reach me—'tis Beu-lah Land.
here there's naught can harm me, I am safe for-ev-er in Beu-lah Land.
learn of full sal-va-tion, Glad-ly will I tar-ry in Beu-lah Land.

CHORUS

I'm liv-ing on the moun-tain, un-der-neath a cloud-less sky, I'm

Praise God!

drink-ing at the fountain that nev-er shall run dry, O yes! I'm feast-ing on the

DWELLING IN BEULAH LAND

man-na from a boun-ti-ful sup-ply For I am dwell-ing in Beu-lah Land.

161
Priscilla J. Owens

JESUS SAVES

Wm. J. Kirkpatrick

1. We have heard the joy-ful sound, Je-sus saves, Je-sus saves;
2. Waft it on the roll-ing tide, Je-sus saves, Je-sus saves;
3. Sing a-bove the bat-tle's strife, Je-sus saves, Je-sus saves;
4. Give the winds a might-y voice, Je-sus saves, Je-sus saves;

Spread the ti-dings all a-round, Je-sus saves, Je-sus saves;
Tell to sin-ners far and wide, Je-sus saves, Je-sus saves;
By His death and end-less life, Je-sus saves, Je-sus saves;
Let the na-tions now re-joice,— Je-sus saves, Je-sus saves;

Bear the news to ev-'ry land, Climb the steeps and cross the waves,
Sing, ye is-lands of the sea, Ech-o back, ye o-cean caves,
Sing it soft-ly thru the gloom, When the heart for mer-cy craves,
Shout sal-va-tion full and free, High-est hills and deep-est caves,

On-ward!—'tis our Lord's com-mand, Je-sus saves, Je-sus saves.
Earth shall keep her ju-bi-lee, Je-sus saves, Je-sus saves.
Sing in tri-umph o'er the tomb,— Je-sus saves, Je-sus saves.
This our song of vic-to-ry,— Je-sus saves, Je-sus saves.

162 WHERE HE LEADS ME

E. W. Blandly

J. S. Norris

1. I can hear my Sav-iour call-ing, I can hear my Sav-iour call-ing,
2. I'll go with Him thru the gar-den, I'll go with Him thru the gar-den,
3. I'll go with Him thru the judgment, I'll go with Him thru the judg-ment,
4. He will give me grace and glo-ry, He will give me grace and glo-ry,

REF.—*Where He leads me I will fol - low, Where He leads me I will fol - low,*

I can hear my Sav-iour call-ing, "Take thy cross and fol-low, fol - low Me."
I'll go with Him thru the gar-den, I'll go with Him, with Him all the way.
I'll go with Him thru the judg-ment, I'll go with Him, with Him all the way.
He will give me grace and glo-ry, And go with me, with me all the way.

Where He leads me I will fol - low, I'll go with Him, with Him all the way.

163 NOTHING BUT THE BLOOD

R. L.

Robert Lowry

1. What can wash a-way my sin? Noth-ing but the blood of Je-sus;
2. For my par-don this I see— Noth-ing but the blood of Je-sus;
3. Noth-ing can for sin a-tone— Noth-ing but the blood of Je-sus;
4. This is all my hope and peace—Noth-ing but the blood of Je-sus;

What can make me whole a-gain? Noth-ing but the blood of Je-sus.
For my cleans-ing this my plea—Noth-ing but the blood of Je-sus.
Naught of good that I have done—Noth-ing but the blood of Je-sus.
This is all my right-eous-ness—Noth-ing but the blood of Je-sus.

NOTHING BUT THE BLOOD

Refrain

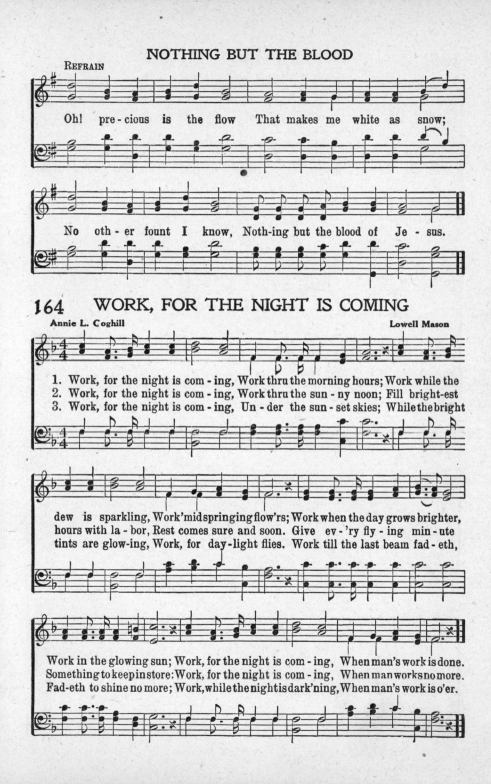

Oh! pre-cious is the flow That makes me white as snow;

No oth-er fount I know, Noth-ing but the blood of Je - sus.

164 WORK, FOR THE NIGHT IS COMING

Annie L. Coghill

Lowell Mason

1. Work, for the night is com-ing, Work thru the morning hours; Work while the
2. Work, for the night is com-ing, Work thru the sun-ny noon; Fill bright-est
3. Work, for the night is com-ing, Un-der the sun-set skies; While the bright

dew is sparkling, Work 'mid springing flow'rs; Work when the day grows brighter,
hours with la-bor, Rest comes sure and soon. Give ev-'ry fly-ing min-ute
tints are glow-ing, Work, for day-light flies. Work till the last beam fad-eth,

Work in the glowing sun; Work, for the night is com-ing, When man's work is done.
Something to keep in store: Work, for the night is com-ing, When man works no more.
Fad-eth to shine no more; Work, while the night is dark'ning, When man's work is o'er.

165 FAITH IS THE VICTORY

John H. Yates

Ira D. Sankey

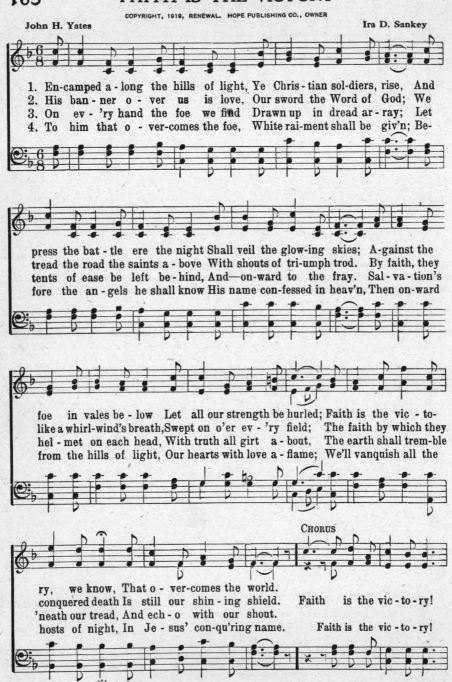

1. En-camped a-long the hills of light, Ye Chris-tian sol-diers, rise, And
2. His ban-ner o-ver us is love, Our sword the Word of God; We
3. On ev-'ry hand the foe we find Drawn up in dread ar-ray; Let
4. To him that o-ver-comes the foe, White rai-ment shall be giv'n; Be-

press the bat-tle ere the night Shall veil the glow-ing skies; A-gainst the
tread the road the saints a-bove With shouts of tri-umph trod. By faith, they
tents of ease be left be-hind, And—on-ward to the fray. Sal-va-tion's
fore the an-gels he shall know His name con-fessed in heav'n, Then on-ward

foe in vales be-low Let all our strength be hurled; Faith is the vic-to-
like a whirl-wind's breath, Swept on o'er ev-'ry field; The faith by which they
hel-met on each head, With truth all girt a-bout, The earth shall trem-ble
from the hills of light, Our hearts with love a-flame; We'll vanquish all the

CHORUS

ry, we know, That o-ver-comes the world.
conquered death Is still our shin-ing shield. Faith is the vic-to-ry!
'neath our tread, And ech-o with our shout.
hosts of night, In Je-sus' con-qu'ring name. Faith is the vic-to-ry!

FAITH IS THE VICTORY

Faith is the vic-to-ry! O glo-ri-ous vic-to-ry, That o-ver-comes the world.
Faith is the vic-to-ry!

166 MY HOPE IS BUILT

Edward Mote

William B. Bradbury

1. My hope is built on noth-ing less Than Je-sus' blood and right-eous-ness;
2. When darkness veils His love-ly face, I rest on His un-chang-ing grace;
3. His oath, His cov-e-nant, His blood, Sup-port me in the whelm-ing flood;
4. When He shall come with trumpet sound, O may I then in Him be found;

I dare not trust the sweet-est frame, But whol-ly lean on Je-sus' name.
In ev-'ry high and storm-y gale, My an-chor holds with-in the veil.
When all a-round my soul gives way, He then is all my hope and stay.
Dressed in His right-eous-ness a-lone, Fault-less to stand be-fore the throne.

REFRAIN

On Christ, the sol-id Rock, I stand; All oth-er ground is

sink-ing sand, All oth-er ground is sink-ing sand. A-MEN.

167 I HEARD THE VOICE OF JESUS SAY

Horatius Bonar

Old English Air

1. I heard the voice of Je-sus say, "Come un-to Me and rest;
2. I heard the voice of Je-sus say, "Be-hold, I free-ly give
3. I heard the voice of Je-sus say, "I am this dark world's Light;

Lay down, thou wea-ry one, lay down Thy head up-on My breast!"
The liv-ing wa-ter; thirst-y one, Stoop down, and drink, and live!"
Look un-to Me, thy morn shall rise, And all thy day be bright!"

I came to Je-sus as I was, Wea-ry, and worn, and sad;
I came to Je-sus, and I drank Of that life-giv-ing stream;
I looked to Je-sus, and I found In Him my Star, my Sun;

I found in Him a rest-ing-place, And He has made me glad.
My thirst was quenched, my soul re-vived, And now I live in Him.
And in that light of life I'll walk, Till trav-'ling days are done.

HE LEADETH ME

Joseph H. Gilmore

William B. Bradbury

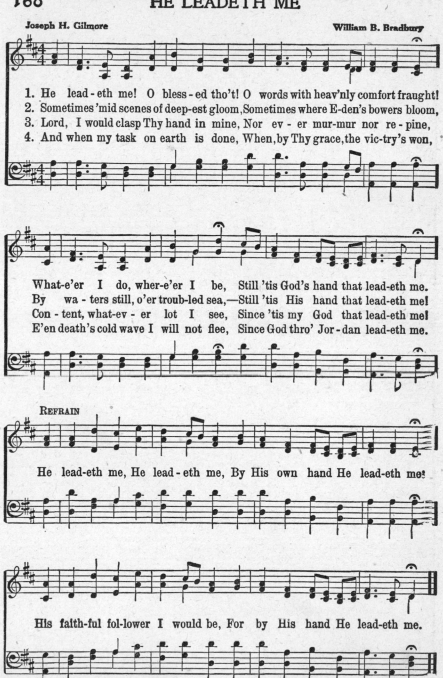

1. He lead-eth me! O bless-ed tho't! O words with heav'nly comfort fraught!
2. Sometimes 'mid scenes of deep-est gloom, Sometimes where E-den's bowers bloom,
3. Lord, I would clasp Thy hand in mine, Nor ev - er mur-mur nor re - pine,
4. And when my task on earth is done, When, by Thy grace, the vic-try's won,

What-e'er I do, wher-e'er I be, Still 'tis God's hand that lead-eth me.
By wa - ters still, o'er troub-led sea,—Still 'tis His hand that lead-eth me!
Con - tent, what-ev - er lot I see, Since 'tis my God that lead-eth me!
E'en death's cold wave I will not flee, Since God thro' Jor - dan lead-eth me.

REFRAIN

He lead-eth me, He lead-eth me, By His own hand He lead-eth me!

His faith-ful fol-lower I would be, For by His hand He lead-eth me.

STILL SWEETER EVERY DAY

W. C. Martin COPYRIGHT, 1927, BY C. AUSTIN MILES, RENEWAL C. Austin Miles

1. To Je-sus ev-'ry day I find my heart is clos-er drawn; He's
2. His glo-ry broke up-on me when I saw Him from a-far: He's
3. My heart is some-times heav-y, but He comes with sweet re-lief; He

fair-er than the glo-ry of the gold and pur-ple dawn; He's all my
fair-er than the lil-y, bright-er than the morn-ing star; He fills and
folds me to His bos-om when I drop with blighting grief; I love the

fan-cy pic-tures in its fair-est dreams, and more; Each day He grows still
sat-is-fies my long-ing spir-it o'er and o'er; Each day He grows still
Christ who all my bur-dens in His bod-y bore; Each day He grows still

CHORUS.

sweet-er than He was the day be-fore. The half......... cannot be
sweet-er than He was the day be-fore.
sweet-er than He was the day be-fore. The half can-not be fan-cied on this

fan - cied this side......... the golden shore; O
side the gold-en shore, The half can-not be fan-cied on this side the golden shore; O

170   I WOULD BE TRUE

Howard Arnold Walter
Author of 3d stanza unknown

Joseph Yates Peek

171 SWEETER AS THE YEARS GO BY

Mrs. C. H. M. Mrs. C. H. Morris

1. Of Je-sus' love that sought me, When I was lost in sin; Of won-drous grace that brought me Back to His fold a-gain; Of heights and depths of mer-cy, Far deep-er than the sea, And high-er than the heaven s, My theme shall ev-er be.

2. He trod in old Ju-de-a Life's pathway long a-go; The peo-ple thronged a-bout Him, His sav-ing grace to know; He healed the bro-ken-heart-ed, And caused the blind to see; And still His great heart yearneth In love for e-ven me.

3. 'Twas wondrous love which led Him For us to suf-fer loss— To bear with-out a mur-mur, The an-guish of the cross; With saints redeemed in glo-ry, Let us our voic-es raise, Till heav'n and earth re-ech-o With our Redeemer's praise.

CHORUS

Sweet-er as the years go by, ... Sweet-er as the years go by; Rich-er, full-er, deep-er,

Sweet-er' as the years go by, 'Tis sweet-er as the years go by;

SWEETER AS THE YEARS GO BY

Je - sus' love is sweet - er, Sweet - er as the years go by.

172   ALONE

B. H. P.

Duet

Ben H. Price

1. It was a - lone the Sav-iour prayed In dark Geth-sem-a - ne;
2. It was a - lone the Sav-iour stood In Pi - late's judgment hall;
3. A-lone up - on the cross He hung That oth - ers He might save;
4. Can you re-ject such matchless love? Can you His claim dis-own?

A - lone He drained the bit - ter cup, And suf-fered there for me.
A - lone the crown of thorns He wore, For-sak - en thus by all.
For-sak-en then by God and man, A - lone, His life He gave.
Come, give your all in grat - i - tude, Nor leave Him thus a - lone.

REFRAIN. *Quartet*

A - lone,   a - lone,   He bore it all a-lone;   He
It was a-lone,   yes, all a-lone,   yes, all a-lone;

gave Himself to save His own, He suf-fered, bled and died a-lone, a - lone.

James Montgomery   Spencer Lane

1. In the hour of tri - al, Je - sus, plead for me, Lest by base de-
2. With for - bid - den pleas-ures Would this vain world charm, Or its sor - did
3. Should Thy mer-cy send me Sor - row, toil and woe, Or should pain at-

ni - al I de-part from Thee; When Thou seest me wa - ver, With a
treas-ures Spread to work me harm, Bring to my re-mem-brance Sad Geth-
tend me On my path be - low, Grant that I may nev - er Fail Thy

look re - call, Nor for fear or fa - vor Suf - fer me to fall.
sem - a - ne, Or, in dark - er sem-blance, Cross-crowned Cal-va-ry.
hand to see; Grant that I may ev - er Cast my care on Thee.

174   LET THE BEAUTY OF JESUS

Albert Orsborn   Rev. Tom Jones

Let the beau-ty of Je-sus be seen in me, All His

won-der-ful pas-sion and pu - ri - ty; O Thou Spir-it di - vine,

LET THE BEAUTY OF JESUS

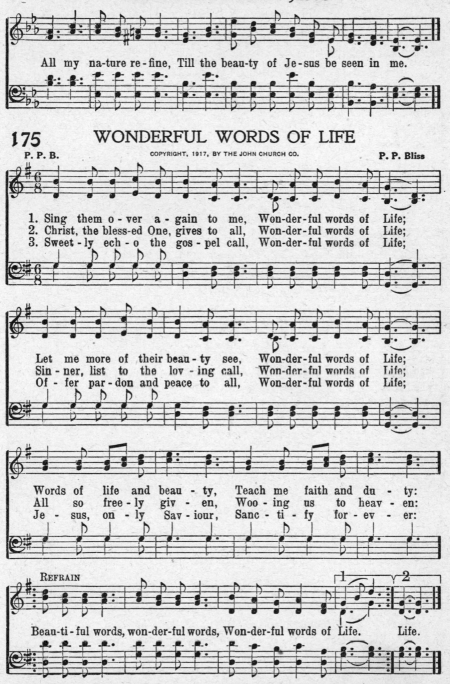

All my na-ture re-fine, Till the beau-ty of Je-sus be seen in me.

175 WONDERFUL WORDS OF LIFE

P. P. B.

COPYRIGHT, 1917, BY THE JOHN CHURCH CO.

P. P. Bliss

1. Sing them o-ver a-gain to me, Won-der-ful words of Life;
2. Christ, the bless-ed One, gives to all, Won-der-ful words of Life;
3. Sweet-ly ech-o the gos-pel call, Won-der-ful words of Life;

Let me more of their beau-ty see, Won-der-ful words of Life;
Sin-ner, list to the lov-ing call, Won-der-ful words of Life;
Of-fer par-don and peace to all, Won-der-ful words of Life;

Words of life and beau-ty, Teach me faith and du-ty:
All so free-ly giv-en, Woo-ing us to heav-en:
Je-sus, on-ly Sav-iour, Sanc-ti-fy for-ev-er:

REFRAIN

Beau-ti-ful words, won-der-ful words, Won-der-ful words of Life. Life.

176 I AM THINE, O LORD

Fanny J. Crosby

W. H. Doane

1. I am Thine, O Lord, I have heard Thy voice, And it
2. Con-se-crate me now to Thy serv-ice, Lord, By the
3. O the pure de-light of a sin-gle hour That be-
4. There are depths of love that I can-not know Till I

told Thy love to me; But I long to rise in the arms of faith,
pow'r of grace di-vine; Let my soul look up with a stead-fast hope,
fore Thy throne I spend, When I kneel in prayer, and with Thee, my God,
cross the nar-row sea; There are heights of joy that I may not reach

And be clos-er drawn to Thee.
And my will be lost in Thine.
I com-mune as friend with friend!
Till I rest in peace with Thee.

REFRAIN

Draw me near-er, near-er, near-er, bless-ed Lord, To the cross where Thou hast died; Draw me near-er, near-er, near-er, bless-ed Lord, To Thy precious, bleed-ing side.

JESUS IS ALL THE WORLD TO ME

W. L. T.

Will L. Thompson

1. Je - sus is all the world to me, My life, my joy, my all;
2. Je - sus is all the world to me, My friend in tri - als sore:
3. Je - sus is all the world to me, And true to Him I'll be;
4. Je - sus is all the world to me, I want no bet - ter friend;

He is my strength from day to day, With - out Him I would fall.
I go to Him for bless - ings, and He gives them o'er and o'er.
Oh, how could I this friend de - ny, When He's so true to me?
I trust Him now, I'll trust Him when Life's fleet - ing days shall end.

When I am sad, to Him I go, No oth - er one can cheer me so;
He sends the sun - shine and the rain, He sends the har - vest's gold - en grain:
Fol - low - ing Him I know I'm right, He watch - es o'er me day and night;
Beau - ti - ful life with such a friend; Beau - ti - ful life that has no end.

When I am sad He makes me glad, He's my friend.
Sun - shine and rain, har - vest of grain, He's my friend.
Fol - low - ing Him, by day and night, He's my friend.
E - ter - nal life, e - ter - nal joy, He's my friend.

178 BACK OF THE CLOUDS

C. R. F.

Carolyn R. Freeman

DUET. Soprano and Alto

1. Nev - er fear tho' shad-ows dark a-round your path may fall; Do not let your
2. Win-ter long is o - ver and the spring has gone her way, Oft - en have the
3. Keep the light of hope e - ter - nal dwell-ing in your heart, Rest up - on the

heart be trou - - bled; From His throne in heav - en, God is
storm-clouds gath - - ered, But the rain has on - ly made the
Fa - ther's prom - - ise, And you'll find that care and trou - ble

watch-ing one and all, .. He will ev - er care for you. .....
blos-soms look more gay, .. Giv - en earth a bright - er hue. .....
quick-ly will de - part, .. Heaven's peace will en - ter in. .....
                                                          care for you,

CHORUS *All, in two parts*

Back of the clouds the sun is al-ways shin-ing, Aft - er the
(Simile)

Four Parts

storms your skies will all be blue; God has pre - pared a
                                                         pre-pared

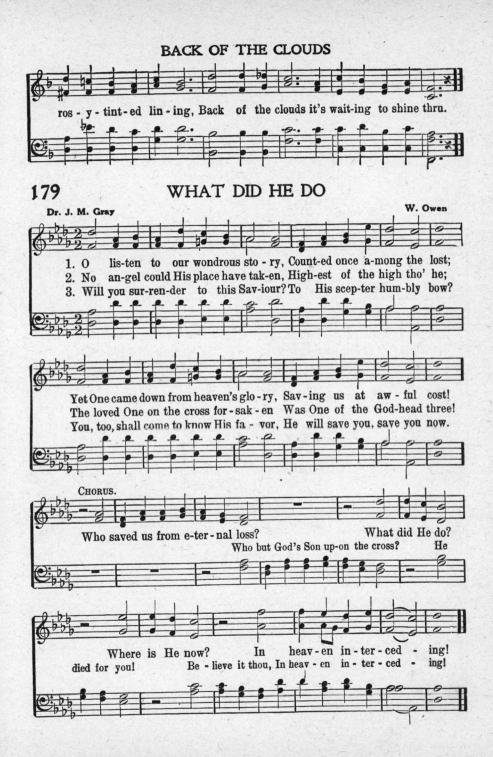

BACK OF THE CLOUDS

ros - y - tint - ed lin - ing, Back of the clouds it's wait-ing to shine thru.

179 WHAT DID HE DO

Dr. J. M. Gray

W. Owen

1. O lis-ten to our wondrous sto-ry, Count-ed once a-mong the lost;
2. No an-gel could His place have tak-en, High-est of the high tho' he;
3. Will you sur-ren-der to this Sav-iour? To His scep-ter hum-bly bow?

Yet One came down from heaven's glo-ry, Sav-ing us at aw-ful cost!
The loved One on the cross for-sak-en Was One of the God-head three!
You, too, shall come to know His fa-vor, He will save you, save you now.

CHORUS.

Who saved us from e-ter-nal loss? What did He do?
Who but God's Son up-on the cross? He

Where is He now? In heav-en in-ter-ced - ing!
died for you! Be-lieve it thou, In heav-en in-ter-ced - ing!

180   DOES JESUS CARE

Frank E. Graeff

J. Lincoln Hall

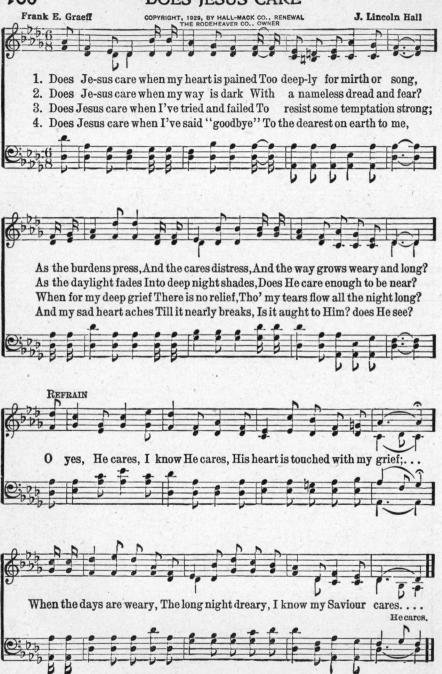

1. Does Je-sus care when my heart is pained Too deep-ly for mirth or song,
2. Does Je-sus care when my way is dark With a nameless dread and fear?
3. Does Jesus care when I've tried and failed To resist some temptation strong;
4. Does Jesus care when I've said "goodbye" To the dearest on earth to me,

As the burdens press, And the cares distress, And the way grows weary and long?
As the daylight fades Into deep night shades, Does He care enough to be near?
When for my deep grief There is no relief, Tho' my tears flow all the night long?
And my sad heart aches Till it nearly breaks, Is it aught to Him? does He see?

REFRAIN

O yes, He cares, I know He cares, His heart is touched with my grief;...

When the days are weary, The long night dreary, I know my Saviour cares. ...

He cares.

LOVE LED HIM TO CALVARY

Geo. O. Webster

Chas. H. Gabriel

1. Love led the Sav-iour, in days long a - go, Down to earth's dark-ness, its
2. Love, for a man-ger, a-ban-doned a throne, Seek - ing the sin - ful, the
3. See - ing the soul in its in - fi-nite worth, Stoop-ing, in love, to the
4. Long-ing, in pit - y, the lost ones to save, Brav-ing the Gar-den, the

sin and its woe; Seek - ing the lost ones, His mer - cy to show,
sad and the lone; Yearn-ing to win them and make them His own,
low - li - est birth, Seek - ing the lost in the by - ways of earth,
Cross and the Grave, Seek - ing this on - ly, the sin - ful to save,

CHORUS *faster*

Love led Him to Cal - va - ry. Love led Him to Cal - va - ry,

Love led Him to Cal - va - ry; Seek - ing the lost, at the

ut - ter - most cost, Love led Him to Cal - va - ry.

John S. B. Monsell

William Boyd

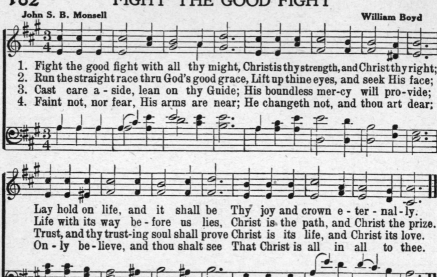

1. Fight the good fight with all thy might, Christ is thy strength, and Christ thy right;
2. Run the straight race thru God's good grace, Lift up thine eyes, and seek His face;
3. Cast care a - side, lean on thy Guide; His boundless mer-cy will pro-vide;
4. Faint not, nor fear, His arms are near; He changeth not, and thou art dear;

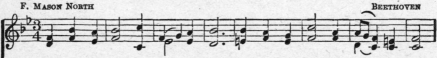

Lay hold on life, and it shall be Thy joy and crown e - ter - nal-ly.
Life with its way be - fore us lies, Christ is the path, and Christ the prize.
Trust, and thy trust-ing soul shall prove Christ is its life, and Christ its love.
On - ly be - lieve, and thou shalt see That Christ is all in all to thee.

183   WHERE CROSS THE CROWDED WAYS OF LIFE

F. Mason North

Beethoven

1. Where cross the crowded ways of life, Where sounds the cries of race and clan,
2. In haunts of wretch-ed - ness and need, On shadowed thresholds dark with fears,
3. The cup of wa - ter giv'n for Thee Still holds the freshness of Thy grace;
4. O Mas-ter, from the mountain side, Make haste to heal these hearts of pain;
5. Till sons of men shall learn Thy love And fol-low where Thy feet have trod:

A - bove the noise of self-ish strife, We hear Thy voice, O Son of man!
From paths where hide the lures of greed, We catch the vi - sion of Thy tears.
Yet long these mul - ti - tudes to see The sweet com-pas-sion of Thy face.
A - mong these restless throngs a-bide, O tread the cit - y's streets a - gain.
Till glo - rious from Thy heav'n above Shall come the cit - y of our God.

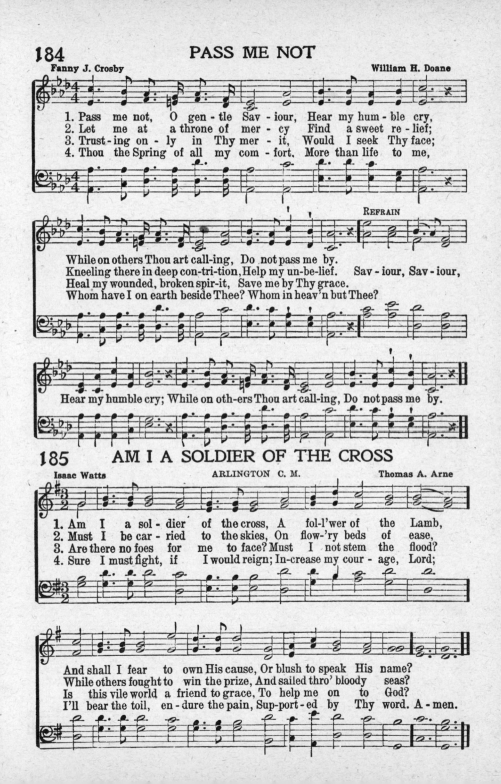

184 PASS ME NOT

Fanny J. Crosby

William H. Doane

1. Pass me not, O gen-tle Sav-iour, Hear my hum-ble cry,
2. Let me at a throne of mer-cy Find a sweet re-lief;
3. Trust-ing on-ly in Thy mer-it, Would I seek Thy face;
4. Thou the Spring of all my com-fort, More than life to me,

REFRAIN

While on others Thou art call-ing, Do not pass me by.
Kneeling there in deep con-tri-tion, Help my un-be-lief.   Sav-iour, Sav-iour,
Heal my wounded, broken spir-it, Save me by Thy grace.
Whom have I on earth beside Thee? Whom in heav'n but Thee?

Hear my humble cry; While on oth-ers Thou art call-ing, Do not pass me by.

185 AM I A SOLDIER OF THE CROSS

Isaac Watts

ARLINGTON C. M.

Thomas A. Arne

1. Am I a sol-dier of the cross, A fol-l'wer of the Lamb,
2. Must I be car-ried to the skies, On flow-'ry beds of ease,
3. Are there no foes for me to face? Must I not stem the flood?
4. Sure I must fight, if I would reign; In-crease my cour-age, Lord;

And shall I fear to own His cause, Or blush to speak His name?
While others fought to win the prize, And sailed thro' bloody seas?
Is this vile world a friend to grace, To help me on to God?
I'll bear the toil, en-dure the pain, Sup-port-ed by Thy word. A-men.

186 OH, IT IS WONDERFUL

C. H. G.

Chas. H. Gabriel

1. I stand all amazed at the love Je-sus of-fers me, Confused at the
2. I mar-vel that He would descend from His throne divine, To res-cue a
3. I think of his hands pierced and bleeding to pay the debt! Such mercy, such

grace that so ful-ly He proffers me; I tremble to know that for me He was
soul so re-bel-lious and proud as mine; That He should extend His great love unto
love and de-vo-tion can I forget? No, no! I will praise and a-dore at the

rit.

cru-ci-fied—That for me, a sin-ner, He suf-fered, He bled, and died.
such as I; Suf-fi-cient to own, to re-deem, and to jus-ti-fy.
mer-cy-seat, Un-til at the glo-ri-fied throne I kneel at His feet.

REFRAIN.

rit.

Oh, it is won-der-ful that He should care for me! E-nough to
won-der-ful!

die for me! Oh, it is won-der-ful, won-der-ful to me!
won-der-ful!

187 IN THE GARDEN

C. A. M.

C. Austin Miles

1. I come to the gar-den a - lone, While the dew is still on the
2. He speaks, and the sound of His voice Is so sweet the birds hush their
3. I'd stay in the gar-den with Him Tho' the night a-round me be

ros - es; And the voice I hear, Fall-ing on my ear; The
sing - ing, And the mel - o - dy That He gave to me, With-
fall - ing, But He bids me go; Thro' the voice of woe, His

CHORUS

Son of God dis - clos - es.
in my heart is ring - ing. And He walks with me, and He
voice to me is call - ing.

talks with me, And He tells me I am His own, And the

joy we share as we tar - ry there, None other has ev - er known.

188 'TIS MIDNIGHT; AND ON OLIVE'S BROW

OLIVE'S BROW. L. M.

William B. Tappan

William B. Bradbury

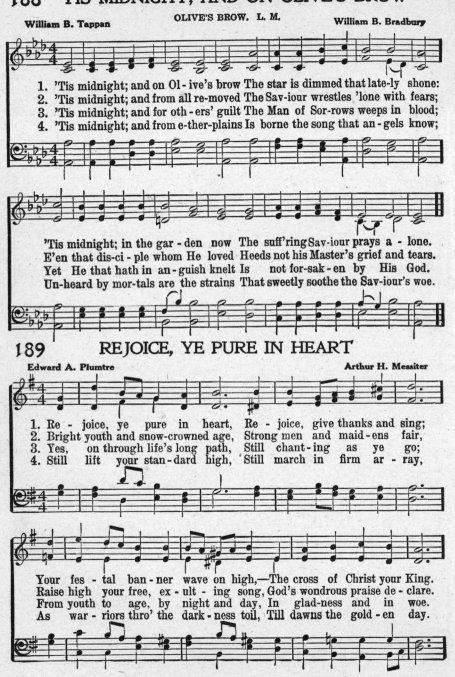

1. 'Tis midnight; and on Ol-ive's brow The star is dimmed that late-ly shone:
2. 'Tis midnight; and from all re-moved The Sav-iour wrestles 'lone with fears;
3. 'Tis midnight; and for oth-ers' guilt The Man of Sor-rows weeps in blood;
4. 'Tis midnight; and from e-ther-plains Is borne the song that an-gels know;

'Tis midnight; in the gar-den now The suff'ring Sav-iour prays a-lone.
E'en that dis-ci-ple whom He loved Heeds not his Master's grief and tears.
Yet He that hath in an-guish knelt Is not for-sak-en by His God.
Un-heard by mor-tals are the strains That sweetly soothe the Sav-iour's woe.

189 REJOICE, YE PURE IN HEART

Edward A. Plumtre

Arthur H. Messiter

1. Re-joice, ye pure in heart, Re-joice, give thanks and sing;
2. Bright youth and snow-crowned age, Strong men and maid-ens fair,
3. Yes, on through life's long path, Still chant-ing as ye go;
4. Still lift your stan-dard high, Still march in firm ar-ray,

Your fes-tal ban-ner wave on high,—The cross of Christ your King.
Raise high your free, ex-ult-ing song, God's wondrous praise de-clare.
From youth to age, by night and day, In glad-ness and in woe.
As war-riors thro' the dark-ness toil, Till dawns the gold-en day.

REJOICE, YE PURE IN HEART

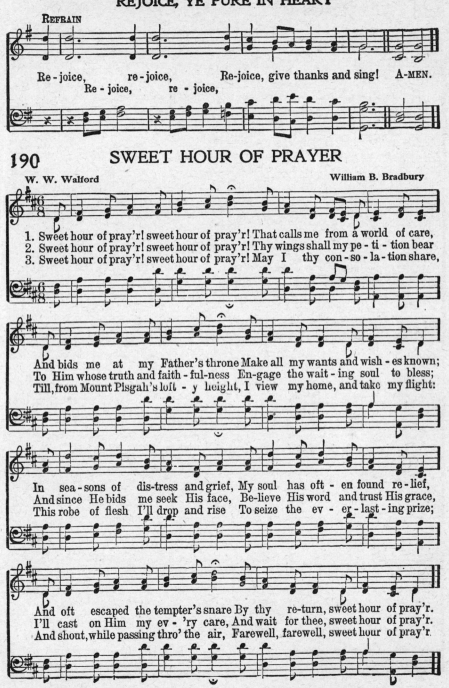

REFRAIN

Re - joice, re - joice, Re-joice, give thanks and sing! A-MEN.
Re - joice, re - joice,

190 SWEET HOUR OF PRAYER

W. W. Walford

William B. Bradbury

1. Sweet hour of pray'r! sweet hour of pray'r! That calls me from a world of care,
2. Sweet hour of pray'r! sweet hour of pray'r! Thy wings shall my pe - ti - tion bear
3. Sweet hour of pray'r! sweet hour of pray'r! May I thy con - so - la - tion share,

And bids me at my Father's throne Make all my wants and wish - es known;
To Him whose truth and faith - ful-ness En-gage the wait - ing soul to bless;
Till, from Mount Pisgah's loft - y height, I view my home, and take my flight:

In sea - sons of dis-tress and grief, My soul has oft - en found re - lief,
And since He bids me seek His face, Be-lieve His word and trust His grace,
This robe of flesh I'll drop and rise To seize the ev - er - last - ing prize;

And oft escaped the tempter's snare By thy re-turn, sweet hour of pray'r.
I'll cast on Him my ev - 'ry care, And wait for thee, sweet hour of pray'r.
And shout, while passing thro' the air, Farewell, farewell, sweet hour of pray'r.

IF YOUR HEART KEEPS RIGHT

Lizzie DeArmond   B. D. Ackley

1. If the dark shadows gath-er As you go a - long, Do not grieve for their
2. Is your life just a tan-gle Full of toil and care? Smile a bit as you
3. There are blossoms of gladness 'Neath the winter's snow, From the gloom and the

com - ing, Sing a cheer - y song, There is joy for the tak-ing it will
jour - ney, Others' bur-dens share; You'll for - get all your troubles, Making
darkness Comes the morning's glow; Nev-er give up the bat - tle, You will

soon be light—Ev - 'ry cloud wears a rainbow If your heart keeps right.
their lives bright, Skies will grow blue and sun-ny If your heart keeps right.
win the fight, Gain the rest of the Vic-tor, If your heart keeps right.

CHORUS

If your heart keeps right, If your heart keeps right, There's a song of

glad-ness in the dark - est night; If your heart keeps right, If your

IF YOUR HEART KEEPS RIGHT

heart keeps right, Ev-'ry cloud will wear a rain-bow, If your heart keeps right.

192 WHAT A FRIEND

JOSEPH SCRIVEN

CHARLES C. CONVERSE

1. What a Friend we have in Je - sus, All our sins and griefs to bear!
2. Have we tri - als and temp - ta - tions? Is there trou-ble an - y-where?
3. Are we weak and heav-y - la - den, Cumbered with a load of care?—

What a priv-i-lege to car - ry Ev - 'ry-thing to God in pray'r!
We should nev - er be dis-cour - aged, Take it to the Lord in pray'r.
Pre - cious Sav-iour, still our ref - uge,—Take it to the Lord in pray'r.

O what peace we oft - en for - feit, O what needless pain we bear,
Can we find a friend so faith - ful Who will all our sor-rows share?
Do thy friends despise, for-sake thee? Take it to the Lord in pray'r;

All because we do not car - ry Ev - 'ry-thing to God in pray'r!
Je - sus knows our ev - 'ry weak - ness, Take it to the Lord in pray'r.
In His arms He'll take and shield thee, Thou wilt find a sol - ace there.

193 I NEED JESUS

GEORGE O WEBSTER

CHAS. H. GABRIEL

1. I need Je-sus, my need I now con-fess; No friend like Him in times of deep dis-tress; I need Je-sus, the need I glad-ly own; Tho' some may bear their load a-lone, Yet I need Je-sus.
2. I need Je-sus, I need a friend like Him, A friend to guide when paths of life are dim; I need Je-sus when foes my soul as-sail; A-lone I know I can but fail,—So I need Je-sus,
3. I need Je-sus, I need Him to the end; No one like Him—He is the sin-ners' Friend; I need Je-sus, no oth-er friend will do; So con-stant, kind, so strong, and true,—Yes, I need Je-sus,

CHORUS

I need Je-sus, I need Je-sus, I need Je-sus ev-'ry day; ev-'ry day; Need Him in the sunshine hour, need Him when the

I need Je-sus with me I need Je-sus al-ways,

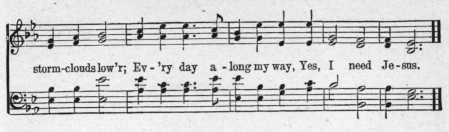

storm-clouds low'r; Ev - 'ry day a - long my way, Yes, I need Je-sus.

194 LET THE LOWER LIGHTS BE BURNING

P. P. B.   Used by permission   P. P. BLISS

1. Bright-ly beams our Fa-ther's mer-cy From His lighthouse ev - er - more;
2. Dark the night of sin has set-tled, Loud the an - gry bil-lows roar;
3. Trim your fee - ble lamp, my brother! Some poor sea - man, tempest-tossed,

But to us He gives the keep-ing Of the lights a - long the shore.
Ea - ger eyes are watching, long-ing, For the lights a - long the shore.
Try - ing now to make the har-bor, In the dark-ness may be lost.

CHORUS

Let the low - er lights be burning! Send a gleam a-cross the wave!

Some poor fainting, struggling sea-man You may res - cue, you may save.

195 TILL THE MORNING

CARLTON C. BUCK

B. D. ACKLEY

1. Wea-ry soul, thou shalt rest in the morn-ing; Thou shalt linger with the blest
2. Ev - 'ry tear shall be dried in the morn-ing; I shall stand by Je-sus' side
3. With the dawn of God's day in the morn-ing; Cares of night shall pass away,

in the morn-ing; Look-ing now beyond life's task Anxious hearts are sure to ask,
in the morn-ing; Nev - er then, to doubt nor fear While my soul keeps asking here,
in that morn-ing; With the tho't of yon-der shore Comes the question o'er and o'er,

CHORUS   pp

"Will it be so ver-y long till the morn - ing." In the morn-ing,

pp

in the morn - ing, It will not be ver-y long till the morn - ing,

With life's bur-dens then laid down We'll re - ceive the prom-ised crown;

TILL THE MORNING

It will not be ver-y long till the morn-ing.

* Small notes last verse only

196 PRAISE HIS NAME

C. H. G.   Chas. H. Gabriel

1. All the way my Lord is lead-ing me, Praise His name, Praise His name!
2. When I faint, His grace up-hold-eth me; Praise His name, Praise His name!
3. Cares of life have o-ver-tak-en me; Praise His name, Praise His name!
Praise............ His name!

With His heav'nly man-na feed-ing me, Praise His ho-ly name.
When I fear, His arms en-fold-eth me, Praise His ho-ly name.
Yet He nev-er has for-sak-en me, Praise His ho-ly name.
Praise His name.

REFRAIN.

Je-sus, Je-sus! This is my song, Je-sus, Je-sus, the whole day long;

He is mine, A Sav-iour di-vine,—Praise His ho-ly name.
Praise His name.

197 SINGING ALONG THE WAY

A. H. A.

Rev. A. H. Ackley

1. Life was meant to be a time of joy and beau-ty, Full of
2. For we know that God is with us, is the rea-son We can
3. Come and join the ran-somed cho-rus, we in-vite you In the

sweet-est mu-sic, too; There's a song for ev-'ry hour of care and
music, too;
sing while oth-ers weep; We can lift the voice of praise in ev-'ry
oth-ers weep;
name of Christ the King; Ev-'ry step you walk with Je-sus will de-
Christ the King;

CHORUS

du-ty, You can sing the whole day thru.
sea-son, And be sure that He will keep. Sing-ing a-
light you, And a new song you will sing.

long (Sing-ing a-long) in days of glad-ness, Sing-ing a-long the way the

rit.

saints have trod, (Sing-ing a-long,) Sing-ing a-long (Sing-ing a-long)

SINGING ALONG THE WAY

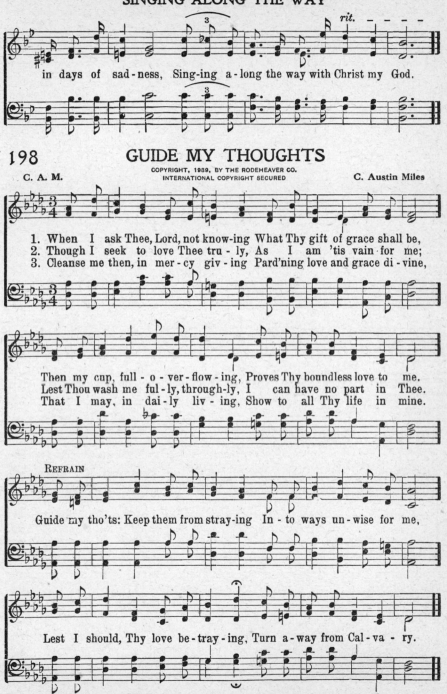

in days of sad-ness, Sing-ing a-long the way with Christ my God.

198 GUIDE MY THOUGHTS

C. A. M.

COPYRIGHT, 1939, BY THE RODEHEAVER CO.
INTERNATIONAL COPYRIGHT SECURED

C. Austin Miles

1. When I ask Thee, Lord, not know-ing What Thy gift of grace shall be,
2. Though I seek to love Thee tru-ly, As I am 'tis vain for me;
3. Cleanse me then, in mer-cy giv-ing Pard'ning love and grace di-vine,

Then my cup, full-o-ver-flow-ing, Proves Thy boundless love to me.
Lest Thou wash me ful-ly, through-ly, I can have no part in Thee.
That I may, in dai-ly liv-ing, Show to all Thy life in mine.

REFRAIN

Guide my tho'ts: Keep them from stray-ing In-to ways un-wise for me,

Lest I should, Thy love be-tray-ing, Turn a-way from Cal-va-ry.

MY REDEEMER

P. P. BLISS

JAMES McGRANAHAN

1. I will sing of my Re-deem-er, And His won-drous love to me;
2. I will tell the won-drous sto - ry, How my lost es - tate to save,
3. I will praise my dear Re-deem-er, His tri - um - phant pow'r I'll tell,
4. I will sing of my Re-deem-er, And His heav'n-ly love to me;

On the cru - el cross He suf-fered, From the curse to set me free.
In His bound-less love and mer-cy, He the ran - som free-ly gave.
How the vic - to - ry He giv - eth O - ver sin, and death, and hell.
He from death to life hath bro't me, Son of God with Him to be.

CHORUS

Sing, oh, sing . . . . of my Re-deem - er,
of my Re-deem - er, Sing, oh, sing of my Re-deem - er,

With His blood . . . . He pur-chased me, ...
He pur-chased me, With His blood He pur-chased me,

On the cross . . . . He sealed my par - don,
He sealed my par - don, On the cross He sealed my par - don,

MY REDEEMER

Paid the debt, ... and made me free. . . . . .
and made me free,
and made me free.

200 JESUS SPREADS HIS BANNER O'ER US

Roswell Park   AUTUMN   Louis von Esch

1. Je-sus spreads His ban-ner o'er us, Cheers our famished souls with food;
2. In Thy ho - ly in - car - na - tion, When the an - gels sang Thy birth;

He the ban-quet spreads be-fore us Of His mys - tic flesh and blood.
In Thy fast - ing and temp-ta - tion, In Thy la - bors on the earth,

Precious ban-quet, bread of heav - en, Wine of glad-ness, flow-ing free;
In Thy tri - al and re - jec - tion, In Thy suff'rings on the tree,

May we taste it, kind - ly giv - en, In re-mem-brance, Lord, of Thee.
In Thy glo - rious res - ur - rec - tion, May we, Lord, re-mem-ber Thee.

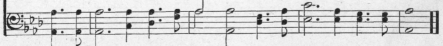

201 I WAS POOR AS THE POOREST

Frank H. Mashaw   J. Lincoln Hall

1. I was poor as the poor-est out-cast from the fold, I
2. I was poor as the poor-est, I shrank from the throng, I
3. I was poor as the poor-est, I wan-dered a-lone, No
4. I was poor as the poor-est, He came from the sky With

sank by the way-side with hun-ger and cold; But He bade me look
hid in the dark-ness that dwelt with me long; But He came like the
place for a dwell-ing, my pil-low a stone; But I heard some-one
love that was death-less for sin-ners to die; And He bled there on

up-ward His rich-es be-hold; O the wealth of the world is Je-sus.
morn-ing with sun-light and song; Now the light of my life is Je-sus.
whis-per,"My child, still My own," Now the peace of my heart is Je-sus.
Cal-v'ry, my heart said,"'Tis I;" Now the love in my soul is Je-sus.

CHORUS

I was poor as the poor-est out-cast from the fold, But He

gave me great treas-ures, Not sil-ver nor gold, But a man-sion up

I WAS POOR AS THE POOREST

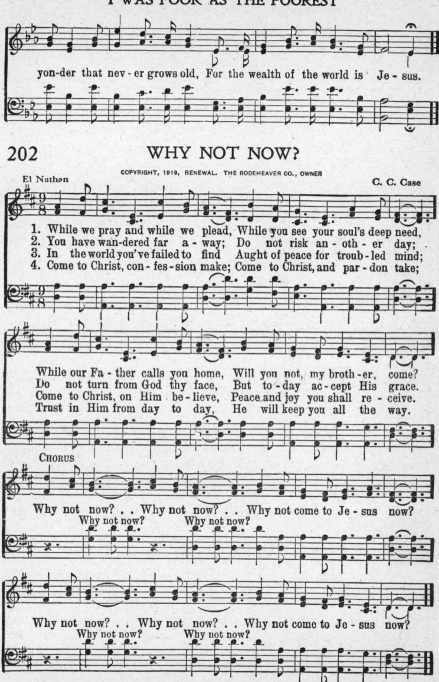

yon-der that nev-er grows old, For the wealth of the world is Je-sus.

202   WHY NOT NOW?

El Nathan

C. C. Case

1. While we pray and while we plead, While you see your soul's deep need,
2. You have wan-dered far a-way; Do not risk an-oth-er day;
3. In the world you've failed to find Aught of peace for troub-led mind;
4. Come to Christ, con-fes-sion make; Come to Christ, and par-don take;

While our Fa-ther calls you home, Will you not, my broth-er, come?
Do not turn from God thy face, But to-day ac-cept His grace.
Come to Christ, on Him be-lieve, Peace and joy you shall re-ceive.
Trust in Him from day to day, He will keep you all the way.

CHORUS

Why not now? . . Why not now? . . Why not come to Je-sus now?
Why not now?   Why not now?

Why not now? . . Why not now? . . Why not come to Je-sus now?
Why not now?   Why not now?

203 REVIVE US AGAIN

Wm. P. Mackay

John J. Husband

1. We praise Thee, O God! for the Son of Thy love, For Je - sus who
2. We praise Thee, O God! for Thy Spir - it of light, Who has shown us our
3. All glo - ry and praise to the Lamb that was slain, Who has borne all our
4. Re - vive us a - gain; fill each heart with Thy love; May each soul be re-

CHORUS

died, and is now gone a - bove.
Sav-iour, and scat-tered our night. Hal-le - lu - jah! Thine the glo - ry, Hal-le-
sins, and has cleansed ev-'ry stain.
kin - dled with fire from a - bove.

lu - jah! A - men; Hal-le - lu - jah! Thine the glo - ry, re - vive us a - gain.

204 THE GREAT PHYSICIAN

Wm. Hunter

J. H. Stockton

1. The great Phy-si - cian now is near, The sym - pa - thiz - ing Je - sus;
2. Your man - y sins are all for-giv'n, O hear the voice of Je - sus;
3. All glo - ry to the dy - ing Lamb, I now be - lieve in Je - sus;
4. His name dis-pels my guilt and fear, No oth - er name but Je - sus;

THE GREAT PHYSICIAN

He speaks the droop-ing heart to cheer, O hear the voice of Je - sus.
Go on your way in peace to heav'n, And wear a crown with Je - sus.
I love the bless - ed Sav-iour's name, I love the name of Je - sus.
Oh! how my soul de-lights to hear The charming name of Je - sus.

D. S.—*Sweet-est car - ol ev - er sung, Je - sus, bless-ed Je - sus.*

REFRAIN

Sweet-est note in ser - aph song, Sweet-est name on mor - tal tongue,

205 COME TO THE SAVIOUR

G. F. R.

George F. Root

1. Come to the Sav-iour, make no de-lay; Here in His Word He's shown us the way;
2. "Suf - fer the children!" Oh, hear His voice, Let ev'ry heart leap forth and re-joice,
3. Think once again, He's with us to-day; Heed now His blest commands, and o-bey;

Here in our midst He's stand-ing to - day, Ten-der-ly say-ing, "Come!"
And let us free - ly make Him our choice, Do not de - lay, but come.
Hear now His ac - cents ten-der-ly say, "Will you, My chil-dren, come?"

D.S.—*And we shall gath - er, Sav - iour, with Thee, In our e - ter - nal home.*

CHORUS

Joy-ful, joy-ful will the meeting be, When from sin our hearts are pure and free;

FOLLOW ME

George D. Watson

Har. by Herbert G. Tovey

DUET

1. I hear my ris-en Sav-iour say...... "Fol-low me, fol-low me, fol-low
2. Tho' thou hast sinned I'll pardon thee,... "Fol-low me, fol-low me, fol-low
3. Come, cast on me thy man-y cares,... "Fol-low me, fol-low me, fol-low

me," His voice is calling all the day,..... "Follow me, follow me, follow me."
me," From ev-'ry sin I'll pardon thee,... "Follow me, follow me, follow me."
me," Thy heav-y load my arm up-bears— "Follow me, follow me, follow me."

FULL CHORUS. (Or Soprano and Alto Duet.)

For thee I trod the bit-ter way,........ For thee I gave my life a-way,
In all thy changing life I'll be........... Thy God, thy guide on land and sea,
Lean on my breast, dismiss thy fears,...... And trust me with thy fu-ture years;

the bitter way,

DUET   ad lib.

And drank the gall thy debt to pay,........... "Follow me, follow me, fol-low me."
Thy blood thro' all e-ter-ni-ty,........... "Follow me, follow me, fol-low me."
My hand shall wipe away all tears,........ "Follow me, follow me, fol-low me."

thy debt to pay,

207 WORK IN EARNEST

C. Austin Miles

B. D. Ackley

1. Work in ear-nest for the One Who in love has sought you; It is Christ, the
2. Conscious of His pow'r with-in, On His strength de-pend-ing, Do not fear the
3. Rest your cause upon the Lord, All to Him con - fid - ing; Build your hope up-

Fa-ther's Son, He your best de-mands. Fear not! You shall soon behold What your
hosts of sin, Mighty tho' they be; Down the highway from the throne, God, in-
on His word, It will stand the test. Thru the conflict and the strife Close to

faith has bro't you;—From the clouds of flaming gold—God's al-might-y hands.
deed, is send-ing Un-to them He calls His own, Cer-tain vic-to-ry.
Him a-bid-ing, Soon will come e-ter-nal life And e-ter-nal rest.

CHORUS

On-ward, Keep your ban-ners ev-er wav-ing; On-ward, For the
On, on, on, On, on, on,

vic-to-ry is sure; We will wear the victor's crown If we to the end en-dure.

208

O HAPPY DAY

PHILIP DODDRIDGE   E. F. RIMBAULT

1. { O hap-py day that fixed my choice On Thee, my Sav-ior and my God! }
   { Well may this glow-ing heart re-joice, And tell its rap-tures all a-broad. }

2. { O hap-py bond, that seals my vows To Him who mer-its all my love! }
   { Let cheerful an-thems fill His house, While to that sa-cred shrine I move. }

3. { 'Tis done: the great transaction's done; I am my Lord's and He is mine; }
   { He drew me, and I followed on, Charmed to con-fess the voice di-vine. }

4. { Now rest, my long-di-vid-ed heart; Fixed on this bliss-ful cen-tre, rest; }
   { Nor ev-er from my Lord de-part, With Him of ev-'ry good possessed. }

FINE

Hap-py day, hap-py day, When Je-sus washed my sins a-way!

D. S.

He taught me how to watch and pray, And live re-joic-ing ev-'ry day;

209

CLOSE TO THEE

FANNY J. CROSBY   SILAS J. VAIL

1. Thou, my ev-er-last-ing por-tion, More than friend or life to me;
2. Not for ease or world-ly pleas-ure, Nor for fame my pray'r shall be;
3. Lead me through the vale of shad-ows, Bear me o'er life's fit-ful sea;

FINE

D.S.–All a-long my pil-grim jour-ney Sav-iour, let me walk with Thee.
D.S.–Glad-ly will I toil and suf-fer, On-ly let me walk with Thee.
D.S.–Then the gate of life e-ter-nal May I en-ter, Lord, with Thee.

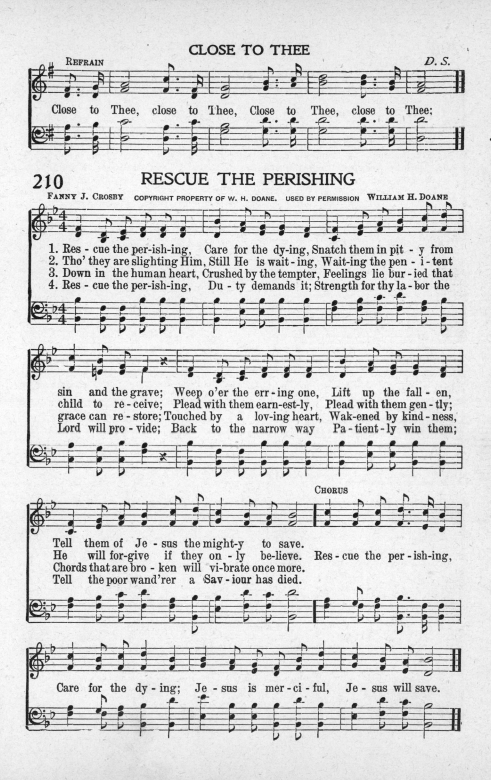

CLOSE TO THEE

REFRAIN

Close to Thee, close to Thee, Close to Thee, close to Thee;

210 RESCUE THE PERISHING

FANNY J. CROSBY   COPYRIGHT PROPERTY OF W. H. DOANE.   USED BY PERMISSION   WILLIAM H. DOANE

1. Res - cue the per-ish-ing, Care for the dy-ing, Snatch them in pit - y from
2. Tho' they are slighting Him, Still He is wait-ing, Wait-ing the pen - i - tent
3. Down in the human heart, Crushed by the tempter, Feelings lie bur - ied that
4. Res - cue the per-ish-ing, Du - ty demands it; Strength for thy la - bor the

sin and the grave; Weep o'er the err - ing one, Lift up the fall - en,
child to re - ceive; Plead with them earn-est-ly, Plead with them gen - tly;
grace can re - store; Touched by a lov-ing heart, Wak-ened by kind - ness,
Lord will pro - vide; Back to the narrow way Pa - tient - ly win them;

CHORUS

Tell them of Je - sus the might-y to save.
He will for-give if they on - ly be-lieve.   Res - cue the per - ish-ing,
Chords that are bro - ken will vi-brate once more.
Tell the poor wand'rer a Sav - iour has died.

Care for the dy - ing; Je - sus is mer - ci - ful, Je - sus will save.

211 AS A VOLUNTEER

W. S. Brown

Chas. H. Gabriel

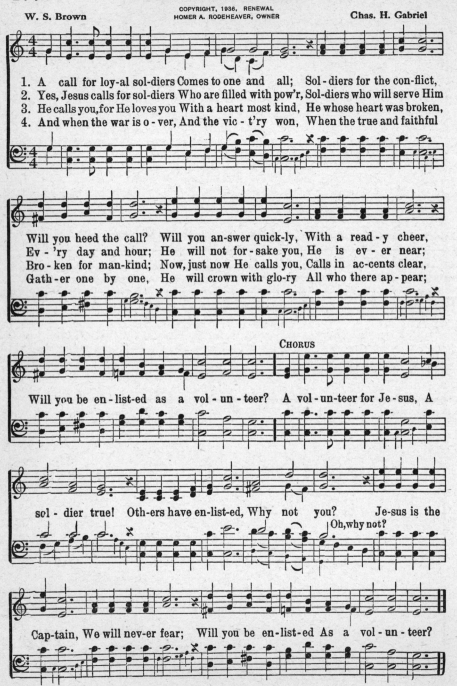

1. A call for loy-al sol-diers Comes to one and all; Sol-diers for the con-flict,
2. Yes, Jesus calls for sol-diers Who are filled with pow'r, Sol-diers who will serve Him
3. He calls you, for He loves you With a heart most kind, He whose heart was broken,
4. And when the war is o-ver, And the vic-t'ry won, When the true and faithful

Will you heed the call? Will you an-swer quick-ly, With a read-y cheer,
Ev-'ry day and hour; He will not for-sake you, He is ev-er near;
Bro-ken for man-kind; Now, just now He calls you, Calls in ac-cents clear,
Gath-er one by one, He will crown with glo-ry All who there ap-pear;

CHORUS

Will you be en-list-ed as a vol-un-teer? A vol-un-teer for Je-sus, A

sol-dier true! Oth-ers have en-list-ed, Why not you? Je-sus is the
Oh, why not?

Cap-tain, We will nev-er fear; Will you be en-list-ed As a vol-un-teer?

212 IS IT THE CROWNING DAY?

COPYRIGHT, 1938, RENEWAL
THE RODEHEAVER CO., OWNER

George Walker Whitcomb

Charles H. Marsh

1. Je - sus may come to - day, Glad day, Glad day! And I would see my
2. I may go home to - day, Glad day, Glad day! Seemeth I hear their
3. Why should I anxious be? Glad day, Glad day! Lights appear on the
4. Faith-ful I'll be to - day, Glad day, Glad day! And I will free - ly

Friend; Dangers and troubles would end If Je - sus should come to -
song; Hail to the ra - di - ant throng! If I should go home to -
shore, Storms will affright nev - er - more, For He is "at hand" to -
tell Why I should love Him so well, For He is my all to -

REFRAIN.

day. Glad day, Glad day! Is it the crown - ing day? I'll

live for to - day, nor anx - ious be; Je - sus, my Lord I

soon shall see. Glad day, Glad day! Is it the crown-ing day?

213 TAKE UP THY CROSS

A. H. A.   REV. A. H. ACKLEY.

Slowly, with expression.

1. I walked one day a-long a coun-try road, And there a stranger journeyed, too,
2. I cried, "Lord Jesus," and He spoke my name; I saw His hands all bruised and torn;
3. "O let me bear Thy cross, dear Lord," I cried, And, lo, a cross for me appeared,
4. My cross I'll car-ry till the crown appears, The way I jour-ney soon will end

Bent low beneath the bur-den of His load: It was a cross, a cross I knew.
I stooped to kiss away the marks of shame, The shame for me that He had borne.
The one for-got-ten I had cast a-side, The one, so long, that I had feared.
Where God Himself shall wipe a-way all tears, And friend hold fellowship with friend.

CHORUS

"Take up thy cross and fol-low Me." I hear the bless-ed Sav-iour call;

How can I make a less-er sac-ri-fice, When Je-sus gave His all?

214 SUNRISE

W. C. Poole

B. D. Ackley

1. When I shall come to the end of my way, When I shall rest at the close of life's day, When "Wel-come home" I shall hear Je-sus say, O that will be sun-rise for me. . . . .

2. When in His beau-ty I see the great King, Join with the ran-somed His prais-es to sing, When I shall join them my trib-utes to bring, O

3. When life is o-ver and day-light is passed, In heav-en's har-bor my an-chor is cast, When I see Je-sus my Sav-iour at last, O

CHORUS

Sun-rise to-mor-row, sun-rise to-mor-row, Sun-rise in glo-ry is wait-ing for me; Sun-rise to-mor-row, sun-rise to-mor-row, Sun-rise with Je-sus for e-ter-ni-ty.

215 JESUS WHISPERS PEACE

D. M. W.   DELLA McCHAIN WARREN

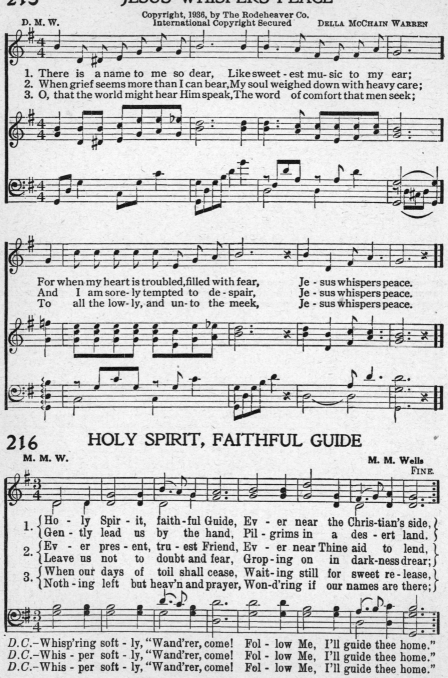

1. There is a name to me so dear, Like sweet-est mu-sic to my ear;
2. When grief seems more than I can bear, My soul weighed down with heavy care;
3. O, that the world might hear Him speak, The word of comfort that men seek;

For when my heart is troubled, filled with fear,   Je-sus whispers peace.
And   I am sore-ly tempted to de-spair,   Je-sus whispers peace.
To   all the low-ly, and un-to the meek,   Je-sus whispers peace.

216 HOLY SPIRIT, FAITHFUL GUIDE

M. M. W.   M. M. Wells
                                               FINE.

1. { Ho-ly Spir-it, faith-ful Guide, Ev-er near the Chris-tian's side,
     Gen-tly lead us by the hand, Pil-grims in a des-ert land. }
2. { Ev-er pres-ent, tru-est Friend, Ev-er near Thine aid to lend,
     Leave us not to doubt and fear, Grop-ing on in dark-ness drear; }
3. { When our days of toil shall cease, Wait-ing still for sweet re-lease,
     Noth-ing left but heav'n and prayer, Won-d'ring if our names are there; }

D.C.—Whisp'ring soft-ly, "Wand'rer, come! Fol-low Me, I'll guide thee home."
D.C.—Whis-per soft-ly, "Wand'rer, come! Fol-low Me, I'll guide thee home."
D.C.—Whis-per soft-ly, "Wand'rer, come! Fol-low Me, I'll guide thee home."

HOLY SPIRIT, FAITHFUL GUIDE

D. C.

Wea - ry souls for - e'er re - joice, While they hear the sweet - est voice,
When the storms are rag - ing sore, Hearts grow faint and hopes give o'er,
Wad - ing deep the dis - mal flood, Plead - ing naught but Je - sus' blood,

217 A LITTLE MORE AND LESS

C. A. M.

C. Austin Miles

A lit-tle more giv-ing, a lit-tle less greed, A lit-tle more thinking of oth-ers in need,

A lit-tle more cour-age to do what is right, Will brighten the moments of earth's darkest night.

A lit-tle more trust in the will of the Lord, More of be-liev-ing His marvelous Word, A

lit-tle less wor-ry of what may come, Will make a bet-ter life and a hap-pi-er home.

218 ALMOST PERSUADED

P. P. B.

P. P. Bliss

1. "Al - most per-suad - ed," now to be - lieve; "Al - most per-suad - ed,"
2. "Al - most per-suad - ed," come, come to - day; "Al - most per-suad - ed,"
3. "Al - most per-suad - ed," har - vest is past! "Al - most per-suad - ed,"

Christ to re - ceive; Seems now some soul to say, "Go, Spir - it,
turn not a - way; Je - sus in - vites you here, An - gels are
doom comes at last! "Al - most" can - not a - vail; "Al - most" is

go Thy way, Some more con - ven - ient day On Thee I'll call."
lin-g'ring near, Prayers rise from hearts so dear, O wan-d'rer, come.
but to fail! Sad, sad, that bit - ter wail, "Al - most," but lost!

219 ONLY TRUST HIM

J. H. S.

J. H. Stockton

1. Come, ev - 'ry soul by sin op-pressed, There's mer-cy with the Lord,
2. For Je - sus shed His pre-cious blood, Rich bless-ings to be - stow;
3. Yes, Je - sus is the Truth, the Way, That leads you in - to rest:

And He will sure - ly give you rest By trust-ing in His Word.
Plunge now in - to the crim - son flood That wash-es white as snow.
Be - lieve in Him with-out de - lay, And you are ful - ly blest.

ONLY TRUST HIM

REFRAIN

On - ly trust Him, on - ly trust Him, On - ly trust Him now;
He will save you, He will save you, He will (*Omit. . . .*) save you now.

220 THE CLEANSING WAVE

Mrs. Phœbe Palmer

Mrs. Joseph F. Knapp

1. Oh, now I see the crim - son wave, The foun - tain deep and wide;
2. I see the new cre - a - tion rise, I hear the speak - ing blood;
3. I rise to walk in heav'n's own light, A - bove the world and sin;
4. A - maz - ing grace! 'tis heav'n be - low, To feel the blood ap - plied;

Je - sus, my Lord, might - y to save, Points to His wound - ed side.
It speaks! pol - lut - ed na - ture dies — Sinks 'neath the crim - son flood.
With hearts made pure and garments white, And Christ enthroned with - in.
And Je - sus, on - ly Je - sus know, My Je - sus cru - ci - fied.

CHORUS

The cleans - ing stream I see, I see! I plunge, and oh, it cleans - eth me;

Oh, praise the Lord, it cleans - eth me, It cleans - eth me, yes, cleans - eth me.

221 HE KEEPS ME SINGING

L. B. B.

COPYRIGHT, 1938, RENEWAL
ROBERT A. COLEMAN, OWNER

L. B. BRIDGERS

1. There's within my heart a mel - o - dy Je - sus whis-pers sweet and low,
2. All my life was wrecked by sin and strife, Dis-cord filled my heart with pain,
3. Feast - ing on the rich - es of His grace, Resting 'neath His shelt'ring wing,
4. Tho' sometimes He leads thro' waters deep, Tri - als fall a - cross the way,
5. Soon He's com-ing back to wel-come me Far be - yond the star - ry sky;

Fear not, I am with thee, peace, be still, In all of life's ebb and flow.
Je - sus swept across the broken strings, Stirred the slumb'ring chords again.
Al - ways look-ing on His smil - ing face, That is why I shout and sing.
Tho' sometimes the path seems rough and steep, See His footprints all the way.
I shall wing my flight to worlds un-known, I shall reign with Him on high.

CHORUS.

Je - sus, Je - sus, Je - sus,— Sweet-est name I know,

Fills my ev - 'ry long - ing, Keeps me sing-ing as I go. A-MEN.

222 SOME BRIGHT MORNING

Charlotte G. Homer   Chas. H. Gabriel

1. Be not a-wea-ry, for la-bor will cease Some glad morn-ing;
2. Wea-ri-some bur-dens will all be laid down, Some glad morn-ing;
3. La-bor well done shall re-ceive its re-ward, Some glad morn-ing;
4. O what a time of re-joic-ing will come, Some glad morn-ing;
5. There with the loved ones who've gone on be-fore, Some glad morn-ing;

Tur-moil will change in-to in-fi-nite peace, Some bright morn-ing.
Then shall our cross be exchanged for a crown, Some bright morn-ing.
Thou who art faith-ful shall be with the Lord, Some bright morn-ing.
When all the ransomed are gathered at home, Some bright morn-ing.
We shall sing praise to the Lamb ev-er-more, Some bright morn-ing.

CHORUS

Some bright morning, Some glad morn-ing, When the sun is shin-ing

in th' e-ter-nal sky; .... Some bright morn-ing, Some glad

cres.

morn-ing .. We shall see the Lord of Har-vest, By and by.

223 BRIGHTEN THE CORNER WHERE YOU ARE

INA DULEY OGDON

CHAS. H. GABRIEL

1. Do not wait un-til some deed of great-ness you may do, Do not
2. Just a-bove are cloud-ed skies that you may help to clear, Let not
3. Here for all your tal-ent you may sure-ly find a need, Here re-

wait to shed your light a-far, To the man-y du-ties ev-er near you
nar-row self your way de-bar, Tho' in-to one heart a-lone may fall your
flect the Bright and Morning Star, E-ven from your humble hand the bread of

REFRAIN

now be true, Bright-en the cor-ner where you are. Bright-en the cor-ner
song of cheer, Bright-en the cor-ner where you are. Bright-en the cor-ner
life may feed, Bright-en the cor-ner where you are.

where you are! Bright-en the cor-ner where you are! Some one far from
Shine for Je-sus where you are!

har-bor you may guide a-cross the bar, Bright-en the cor-ner where you are.

224 THE WAY OF THE CROSS LEADS HOME

JESSIE BROWN POUNDS   CHAS. H. GABRIEL

1. I must needs go home by the way of the cross, There's no oth-er
2. I must needs go on in the blood-sprinkled way, The path that the
3. Then I bid fare-well to the way of the world, To walk in it

way but this; I shall ne'er get sight of the Gates of Light,
Sav-iour trod, If I ev-er climb to the heights sub-lime,
nev-er-more; For my Lord says "Come," and I seek my home,

CHORUS.

If the way of the cross I miss.
Where the soul is at home with God.   The way of the cross leads
Where He waits at the o-pen door.

home,   The way of the cross leads home;   It is
  leads home,   leads home;

sweet to know, as I on-ward go, The way of the cross leads home. A-MEN.

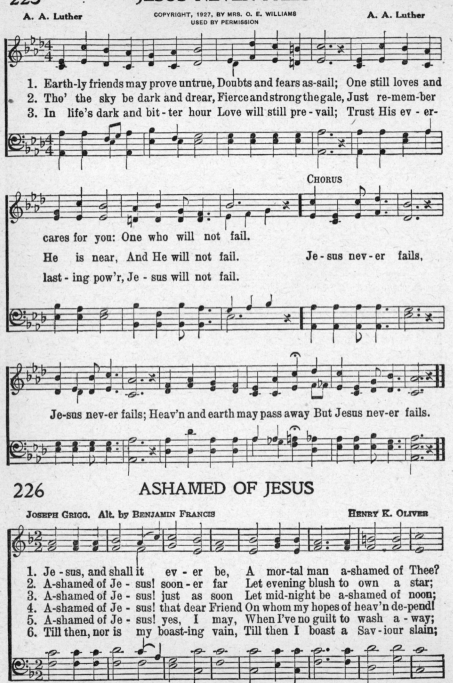

ASHAMED OF JESUS

A-shamed of Thee, whom an - gels praise, Whose glories shine thro' end-less days?
He sheds the beams of light di - vine O'er this be-night-ed soul of mine.
'Tis mid-night with my soul till He, Bright Morning-S r, bid darkness flee.
No; when I blush, be this my shame, That I no more re-v re His name.
No tear to wipe, no good to crave, No fears to quell, no soul to save.
And O, may this my lo - ry be, That Christ is not a-shamed of me!

227 AWAKE, MY SOUL, IN JOYFUL LAYS

Rev. Samuel Medley   Western Melody

1. A - wake, my soul, in joy-ful lays, And sing thy great Re-deem-er's praise;
2. He saw me ru - ined in the fall, Yet loved me not - with-stand-ing all,
3. Thro' might-y hosts of cru - el foes, Where earth and hell my way op - pose,
4. Oft - en I feel my sin - ful heart, Prone from my Je - sus to de - part;

He just-ly claims a song from me, His lov - ing-kind - ness is so free.
And saved me from my lost es - tate, His lov-ing-kind - ness is so great.
He safe-ly leads my soul a - long, His lov-ing-kind - ness is so strong.
And tho' I oft have Him for-got, His lov-ing-kind - ness changes not.

Lov - ing-kind-ness, lov - ing-kind-ness, His lov-ing-kind - ness is so free.
Lov - ing-kind-ness, lov - ing-kind-ness, His lov-ing-kind - ness is so great.
Lov - ing-kind-ness, lov - ing-kind-ness, His lov - ing-kind - ness is so strong.
Lov - ing-kind-ness, lov - ing-kind-ness, His lov - ing-kind - ness changes not.

228 YOU MUST OPEN THE DOOR

ina Duley Ogdon

Homer A. Rodeheaver

1. There's a Sav - ior who stands at the door of your heart, He is
2. He has come from the Fa - ther sal - va - tion to bring, And His
3. He is lov - ing and kind, full of in - fi - nite grace, In your
4. He will lead you at last to that bless - ed a - bode, To the

long - ing to en - ter—why let Him de - part? He has pa - tient - ly
name is called Je - sus, Re - deem - er and King; To save you and
heart, in your life, will you give Him a place? He is wait - ing to
cit - y of God, at the end of the road, Where the night nev - er

called you so oft - en be - fore, But you must o - pen the door.
keep you He pleads ev - er - more, But you must o - pen the door.
bless you, your soul to re - store, But you must o - pen the door.
falls, when life's jour-ney is o'er, But you must o - pen the door.

CHORUS

You must o - pen the door, You must o - pen the door, When

Je - sus comes in, He will save you from sin, But you must o - pen the door.

229 I AM PRAYING FOR YOU

S. O'MALEY CLUFF

IRA D. SANKEY

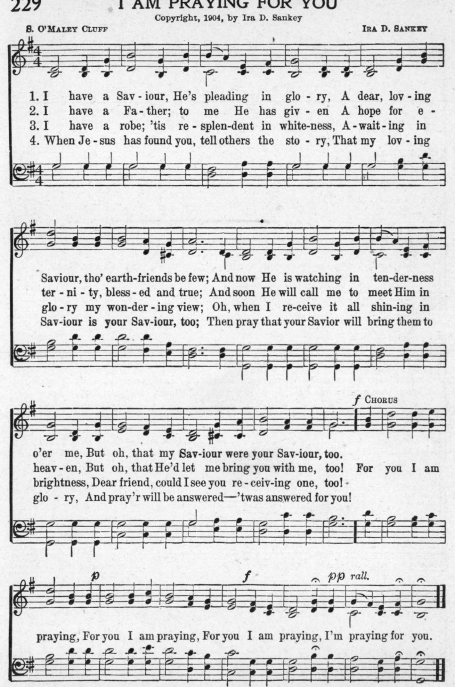

1. I have a Sav-iour, He's pleading in glo-ry, A dear, lov-ing
2. I have a Fa-ther; to me He has giv-en A hope for e-
3. I have a robe; 'tis re-splen-dent in white-ness, A-wait-ing in
4. When Je-sus has found you, tell others the sto-ry, That my lov-ing

Saviour, tho' earth-friends be few; And now He is watching in ten-der-ness
ter-ni-ty, bless-ed and true; And soon He will call me to meet Him in
glo-ry my won-der-ing view; Oh, when I re-ceive it all shin-ing in
Sav-iour is your Sav-iour, too; Then pray that your Savior will bring them to

o'er me, But oh, that my Sav-iour were your Sav-iour, too.
heav-en, But oh, that He'd let me bring you with me, too! For you I am
brightness, Dear friend, could I see you re-ceiv-ing one, too!
glo-ry, And pray'r will be answered—'twas answered for you!

f CHORUS

praying, For you I am praying, For you I am praying, I'm praying for you.

230 TILL THE WHOLE WORLD KNOWS

Rev. A. H. Ackley   B. D. Ackley

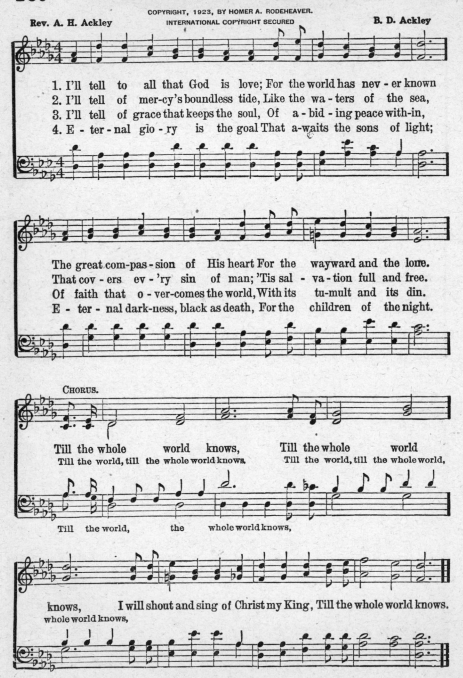

1. I'll tell to all that God is love; For the world has nev-er known
2. I'll tell of mer-cy's boundless tide, Like the wa-ters of the sea,
3. I'll tell of grace that keeps the soul, Of a-bid-ing peace with-in,
4. E-ter-nal glo-ry is the goal That a-waits the sons of light;

The great com-pas-sion of His heart For the wayward and the lone.
That cov-ers ev-'ry sin of man; 'Tis sal-va-tion full and free.
Of faith that o-ver-comes the world, With its tu-mult and its din.
E-ter-nal dark-ness, black as death, For the children of the night.

CHORUS.

Till the whole world knows, Till the whole world
Till the world, till the whole world knows.   Till the world, till the whole world,

Till the world, the whole world knows,

knows, I will shout and sing of Christ my King, Till the whole world knows.
whole world knows,

231 HELP SOMEBODY TO-DAY

MRS. FRANK M. BRECK

CHAS. H. GABRIEL

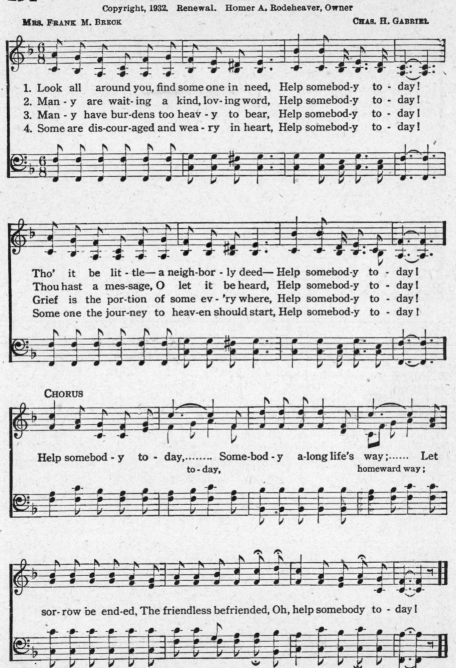

1. Look all around you, find some one in need, Help somebod-y to-day!
2. Man-y are wait-ing a kind, lov-ing word, Help somebod-y to-day!
3. Man-y have bur-dens too heav-y to bear, Help somebod-y to-day!
4. Some are dis-cour-aged and wea-ry in heart, Help somebod-y to-day!

Tho' it be lit-tle— a neigh-bor-ly deed— Help somebod-y to-day!
Thou hast a mes-sage, O let it be heard, Help somebod-y to-day!
Grief is the por-tion of some ev-'ry where, Help somebod-y to-day!
Some one the jour-ney to heav-en should start, Help somebod-y to-day!

CHORUS

Help somebod-y to-day,........ Some-bod-y a-long life's way;...... Let
to-day, homeward way;

sor-row be end-ed, The friendless befriended, Oh, help somebody to-day!

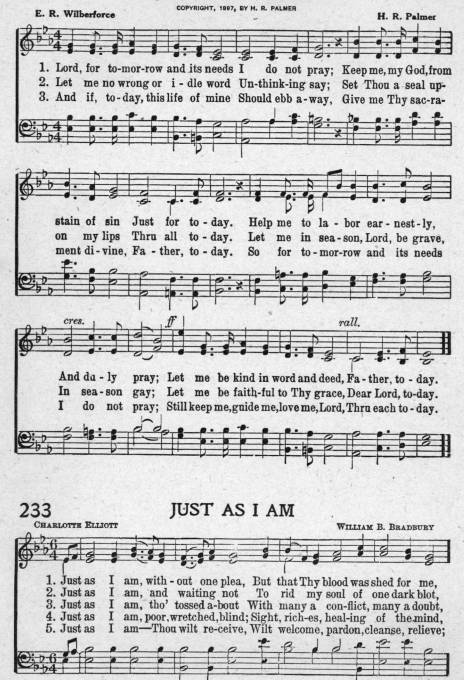

232   JUST FOR TODAY

COPYRIGHT, 1897, BY H. R. PALMER

E. R. Wilberforce

H. R. Palmer

1. Lord, for to-mor-row and its needs I do not pray; Keep me, my God, from
2. Let me no wrong or i-dle word Un-think-ing say; Set Thou a seal up-
3. And if, to-day, this life of mine Should ebb a-way, Give me Thy sac-ra-

stain of sin Just for to-day. Help me to la-bor ear-nest-ly,
on my lips Thru all to-day. Let me in sea-son, Lord, be grave,
ment di-vine, Fa-ther, to-day. So for to-mor-row and its needs

cres.   *ff*   *rall.*

And du-ly pray; Let me be kind in word and deed, Fa-ther, to-day.
In sea-son gay; Let me be faith-ful to Thy grace, Dear Lord, to-day.
I do not pray; Still keep me, guide me, love me, Lord, Thru each to-day.

233   JUST AS I AM

Charlotte Elliott

William B. Bradbury

1. Just as I am, with-out one plea, But that Thy blood was shed for me,
2. Just as I am, and wait-ing not To rid my soul of one dark blot,
3. Just as I am, tho' tossed a-bout With many a con-flict, many a doubt,
4. Just as I am, poor, wretched, blind; Sight, rich-es, heal-ing of the mind,
5. Just as I am—Thou wilt re-ceive, Wilt wel-come, par-don, cleanse, re-lieve;

And that Thou bidd'st me come to Thee, O Lamb of God, I come! I come!
To Thee whose blood can cleanse each spot, O Lamb of God, I come! I come!
Fight-ings and fears with-in, with-out, O Lamb of God, I come! I come!
Yea, all I need in Thee to find, O Lamb of God, I come! I come!
Be - cause Thy promise I be-lieve, O Lamb of God, I come! I come!

234 FAITH OF OUR FATHERS

FREDERICK W. FABER

H. F. HEMY

1. Faith of our fa-thers! liv - ing still In spite of dungeon, fire and sword,
2. Our fathers, chained in pris-ons dark, Were still in heart and conscience free:
3. Faith of our fa-thers! we will love Both friend and foe in all our strife:

O how our hearts beat high with joy Whene'er we hear that glo-rious word!
How sweet would be their children's fate, If they, like them, could die for thee!
And preach thee, too, as love knows how, By kind-ly words and vir-tuous life:

Faith of our fa-thers! ho - ly faith! We will be true to thee till death!
Faith of our fa-thers! ho - ly faith! We will be true to thee till death!
Faith of our fa-thers! ho - ly faith! We will be true to thee till death!

235 MY SAVIOUR'S LOVE

C. H. G.

CHAS. H. GABRIEL

1. I stand a-mazed in the pres-ence Of Je-sus the Naz-a-rene,
2. For me it was in the gar-den He pray'd; "Not My will, but Thine,"
3. In pit-y an-gels be-held Him, And came from the world of light
4. He took my sins and my sor-rows, He made them His ver-y own;
5. When with the ran-som'd in glo-ry His face I at last shall see,

And won-der how He could love me, A sin-ner condem'd, un-clean.
He had no tears for His own griefs, But sweat-drops of blood for mine.
To com-fort Him in the sor-rows He bore for my soul that night.
He bore the bur-den to Cal-v'ry, And suf-fer'd, and died a-lone.
'Twill be my joy thro' the a-ges To sing of His love for me.

CHORUS

How mar-vel-ous! how won-der-ful! And my song shall ev-er be:
Oh, how mar-vel-ous! oh, how won-der-ful!

How mar-vel-ous! how won-der-ful Is my Sav-iour's love for me!
Oh, how mar-vel-ous! oh, how won-der-ful

236 STANDING ON THE PROMISES

R. K. C. Copyright, 1886, by John J. Hood R. KELSO CARTER

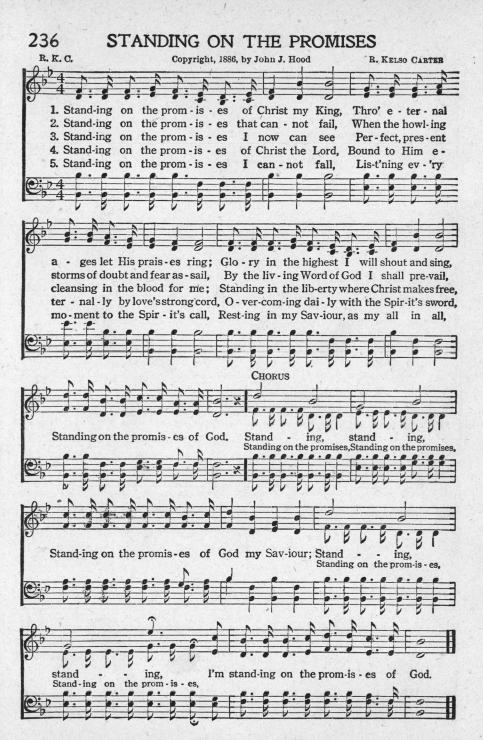

1. Stand-ing on the prom-is-es of Christ my King, Thro' e-ter-nal
2. Stand-ing on the prom-is-es that can-not fail, When the howl-ing
3. Stand-ing on the prom-is-es I now can see Per-fect, pres-ent
4. Stand-ing on the prom-is-es of Christ the Lord, Bound to Him e-
5. Stand-ing on the prom-is-es I can-not fall, Lis-t'ning ev-'ry

a-ges let His prais-es ring; Glo-ry in the highest I will shout and sing,
storms of doubt and fear as-sail, By the liv-ing Word of God I shall pre-vail,
cleansing in the blood for me; Standing in the lib-erty where Christ makes free,
ter-nal-ly by love's strong cord, O-ver-com-ing dai-ly with the Spir-it's sword,
mo-ment to the Spir-it's call, Rest-ing in my Sav-iour, as my all in all,

CHORUS

Standing on the promis-es of God. Stand - ing, stand - ing,
Standing on the promises, Standing on the promises,

Stand-ing on the promis-es of God my Sav-iour; Stand - - ing,
Standing on the prom-is-es,

stand - - ing, I'm stand-ing on the prom-is-es of God.
Stand-ing on the prom-is-es,

237 MORE LIKE THE MASTER

C. H. G.

CHAS. H. GABRIEL

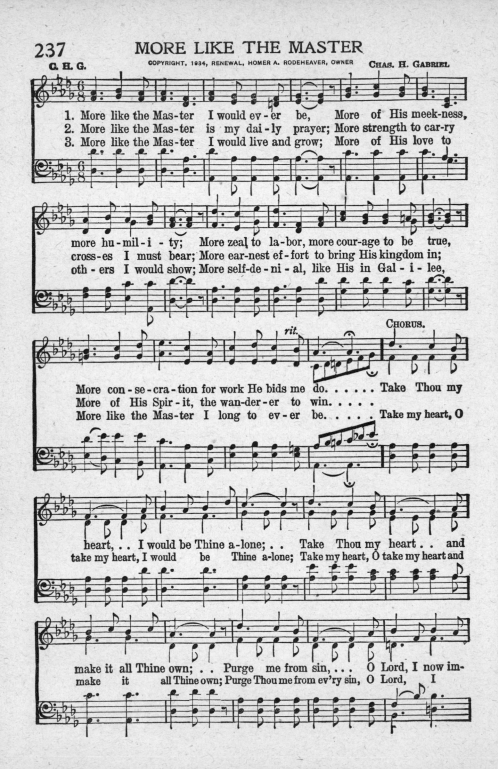

1. More like the Mas-ter I would ev - er be, More of His meek-ness,
2. More like the Mas-ter is my dai-ly prayer; More strength to car-ry
3. More like the Mas-ter I would live and grow; More of His love to

more hu-mil-i-ty; More zeal to la-bor, more cour-age to be true,
cross-es I must bear; More ear-nest ef-fort to bring His kingdom in;
oth-ers I would show; More self-de-ni-al, like His in Gal-i-lee,

rit.

CHORUS.

More con-se-cra-tion for work He bids me do...... Take Thou my
More of His Spir-it, the wan-der-er to win......
More like the Mas-ter I long to ev-er be...... Take my heart, O

heart,... I would be Thine a-lone;.. Take Thou my heart.. and
take my heart, I would be Thine a-lone; Take my heart, O take my heart and

make it all Thine own;.. Purge me from sin,... O Lord, I now im-
make it all Thine own; Purge Thou me from ev'ry sin, O Lord, I

MORE LIKE THE MASTER

plore, . . . Wash me and keep me Thine for - ev - er - more.
now im-plore, Wash and keep, O keep me Thine for - ev - er - more.

238   LEAD ME TO CALVARY

Jennie Evelyn Hussey   Wm. J. Kirkpatrick

1. King of my life, I crown Thee now, Thine shall the glo - ry be;
2. Show me the tomb where Thou wast laid, Ten - der-ly mourned and wept;
3. Let me like Ma - ry, thru the gloom, Come with a gift to Thee;
4. May I be will - ing, Lord, to bear Dai - ly my cross for Thee;

Lest I for-get Thy thorn-crowned brow, Lead me to Cal - va - ry.
An - gels in robes of light ar - rayed Guard-ed Thee whilst Thou slept.
Show to me now the emp - ty tomb, Lead me to Cal - va - ry.
E - ven Thy cup of grief to share, Thou hast borne all for me.

Chorus

Lest I for - get Geth-sem - a - ne; Lest I for - get Thine ag - o - ny;

Lest I for - get Thy love for me, Lead me to Cal - va - ry.

239   O GOD, OUR HELP IN AGES PAST

Isaac Watts

William Croft

1. O God, our help in a-ges past, Our hope for years to come,
2. Be-fore the hills in or-der stood, Or earth re-ceived her frame,
3. A thous-and a-ges, in Thy sight, Are like an ev-'ning gone;
4. Time, like an ev-er-roll-ing stream, Bears all its sons a-way;
5. O God, our help in a-ges past, Our hope for years to come;

Our shel-ter from the storm-y blast, And our e-ter-nal home!
From ev-er-last-ing Thou art God, To end-less years the same.
Short as the watch that ends the night, Be-fore the ris-ing sun.
They fly, for-got-ten, as a dream Dies at the ope-ning day.
Be Thou our guide while life shall last, And our e-ter-nal home! A-men.

240   FATHER, LEAD ME DAY BY DAY

John P. Hopps

Charles H. Gabriel

1. Fa-ther, lead me day by day, Ev-er in Thine own sweet way;
2. When in dan-ger make me brave, Make me know that Thou canst save;
3. When I'm tempt-ed to do wrong, Keep me stead-fast, wise, and strong;
4. May I do the good I know, Serv-ing glad-ly here be-low,

Teach me to be pure and true, Show me what I ought to do.
Keep me safe by Thy dear side; Let me in Thy love a-bide.
And when all a-lone I stand, Shield me with Thy might-y hand.
Then at last go home to Thee, Ev-er-more Thine own to be.

241 SAVIOUR, LIKE A SHEPHERD LEAD US

DOROTHY ANN THRUPP

WILLIAM B. BRADBURY

1. Sav - iour, like a Shep-herd lead us, Much we need Thy ten-der care;
2. We are Thine, do Thou be - friend us, Be the Guardian of our way;
3. Thou hast promised to re - ceive us, Poor and sin-ful tho' we be;
4. Ear - ly let us seek Thy fa - vor; Ear - ly let us do Thy will;

In Thy pleasant pas-tures feed us, For our use Thy folds pre-pare:
Keep Thy flock, from sin de - fend us, Seek us when we go a-stray:
Thou hast mer-cy to re - lieve us, Grace to cleanse, and pow'r to free:
Bless - ed Lord and on - ly Sav - iour, With Thy love our bos-oms fill:

Bless-ed Je - sus, Bless-ed Je - sus, Thou hast bought us, Thine we are;
Bless-ed Je - sus, Bless-ed Je - sus, Hear Thy chil-dren when they pray;
Bless-ed Je - sus, Bless-ed Je - sus, Ear-ly let us turn to Thee;
Bless-ed Je - sus, Bless-ed Je - sus, Thou hast loved us, love us still;

Bless-ed Je - sus, Bless-ed Je - sus, Thou hast bought us, Thine we are.
Bless-ed Je - sus, Bless-ed Je - sus, Hear Thy children when they pray.
Bless-ed Je - sus, Bless-ed Je - sus, Ear-ly let us turn to Thee.
Bless-ed Je - sus, Bless-ed Je - sus, Thou hast loved us, love us still.

242 SOMEBODY'S PRAYING FOR YOU

Ida L. Reed

C. Austin Miles

1. Come to the Fa-ther, O wan-der-er, come, Somebody's praying for you;
2. God's voice is call-ing, O do not de-lay, Somebody's praying for you;
3. Quench not the spir-it but yield from your heart, Somebody's praying for you;

Turn from the sin-paths no lon-ger to roam, Some-bod-y's pray-ing for
Bow at the mer-cy-seat, bend while you may, Some-bod-y's pray-ing for
God waits His par-don, His peace to im-part, Some-bod-y's pray-ing for is

you. . . . Some-bod-y loves you wher-ev-er you stray, Bears you in
you. . . . Some-bod-y's wrestling in prayer for your soul, Long-ing to
you. . . . Kneel in your weakness, con-fess-ing your sin, Tho' they are

pray-ing for you.

faith to God day aft-er day; Prayer-ful-ly fol-lows you all the dark way,
see you made per-fect-ly whole; Down where the bil-lows of Cal-va-ry roll,
man-y and dark tho' they've been; O-pen your heart, let love's cleansing tide in,

Some-bod-y's pray-ing for you, for you. For you I am pray-ing, For

SOMEBODY'S PRAYING FOR YOU

Very softly

you I am pray-ing, For you I am pray-ing, I'm pray-ing for you.

243   JESUS IS CALLING

COPYRIGHT, 1911, BY GEO. C. STEBBINS, RENEWAL
HOPE PUBLISHING CO., OWNER

Fanny J. Crosby

George C. Stebbins

1. Je-sus is ten-der-ly call-ing thee home—Call-ing to-day, call-ing to-day;
2. Je-sus is call-ing the wea-ry to rest—Call-ing to-day, call-ing to-day;
3. Je-sus is wait-ing, O come to Him now—Waiting to-day, wait-ing to-day;
4. Je-sus is pleading, O list to His voice—Hear Him to-day, hear Him to-day;

Why from the sun-shine of love wilt thou roam Far-ther and far-ther a-way?
Bring Him thy bur-den and thou shalt be blest; He will not turn thee a-way.
Come with thy sins, at His feet low-ly bow; Come, and no lon-ger de-lay.
They who be-lieve on His name shall re-joice; Quick-ly a-rise and a-way.

CHORUS

Call - - ing to-day! . . . Call - - ing to-day! . . .
Call-ing, call-ing to-day, to-day! Call-ing, call-ing to-day, to-day!

Je - - sus is call - - ing, Is ten-der-ly call-ing to-day.
Je-sus is ten-der-ly call-ing to-day,

244   BLESSED ASSURANCE

FANNY J. CROSBY   Used by permission   MRS. JOS. F. KNAPP

1. Bless-ed as-sur-ance, Je-sus is mine! O what a fore-taste of
2. Per-fect sub-mis-sion, per-fect de-light, Vi-sions of rap-ture now
3. Per-fect sub-mis-sion, all is at rest, I in my Sav-ior am

glo-ry di-vine! Heir of sal-va-tion, purchase of God, Born of His
burst on my sight! Angels de-scend-ing, bring from a-bove Ech-oes of
hap-py and blest; Watching and waiting, look-ing a-bove, Filled with His

Spir-it, washed in His blood.
mer-cy, whis-pers of love.
good-ness, lost in His love.

CHORUS

This is my sto-ry, this is my song, Prais-ing my Sav-ior all the day long; This is my sto-ry, this is my song, Praising my Sav-iour all the day long.

"WHOSOEVER WILL"

P. P. B.

P. P. BLISS

1. "Who-so-ev-er hear - eth," shout, shout the sound! Spread the bless-ed ti-dings
2. Who-so-ev-er com - eth, need not de - lay, Now the door is o - pen,
3. "Who-so-ev-er will!" the prom-ise is se - cure; "Who-so-ev - er will," for-

all the world a-round; Tell the joy - ful news wher - ev - er man is found,
en - ter while you may; Je - sus is the true, the on - ly Liv-ing Way:
ev - er must en-dure; "Who-so - ev - er will!" 'tis life for - ev - er-more;

CHORUS

"Who-so-ev - er will may come." "Who-so-ev - er will, who-so-ev - er will!"

Send the proc - la - ma - tion o - ver vale and hill; 'Tis a lov - ing

Fa - ther calls the wan-d'rer home: "Who-so - ev - er will may come."

246 THIS IS MY FATHER'S WORLD

Traditional English Melody
Arranged by S. F. L.

MALTBIE D. BABCOCK

1. This is my Fa-ther's world, And to my list-'ning ears, All na-ture sings, and round me rings The mu-sic of the spheres. This is my Fa-ther's world, I rest me in the thought Of rocks and trees, of skies and seas—His hand the won-ders wrought.

2. This is my Fa-ther's world, The birds their car - ols raise, The morn-ing light, the lil - y white, De - clare their Ma - ker's praise. This is my Fa-ther's world, He shines in all that's fair; In the rus-tling grass I hear Him pass, He speaks to me ev-'ry-where,

3. This is my Fa-ther's world, O let me ne'er for - get That though the wrong seems oft so strong, God is the Ru - ler yet. This is my Fa-ther's world, The bat - tle is not done, Je - sus who died shall be sat - is - fied, And earth and heav'n be one. A-men.

247 CROWN HIM WITH MANY CROWNS

MATTHEW BRIDGES

GEORGE J. ELVEY

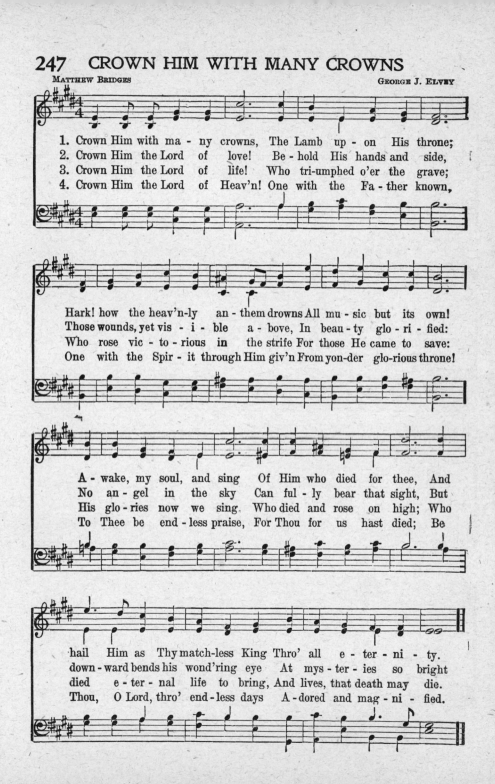

1. Crown Him with ma - ny crowns, The Lamb up - on His throne;
2. Crown Him the Lord of love! Be - hold His hands and side,
3. Crown Him the Lord of life! Who tri-umphed o'er the grave;
4. Crown Him the Lord of Heav'n! One with the Fa - ther known,

Hark! how the heav'n-ly an - them drowns All mu - sic but its own!
Those wounds, yet vis - i - ble a - bove, In beau - ty glo - ri - fied:
Who rose vic - to - rious in the strife For those He came to save:
One with the Spir - it through Him giv'n From yon-der glo-rious throne!

A - wake, my soul, and sing Of Him who died for thee, And
No an - gel in the sky Can ful - ly bear that sight, But
His glo - ries now we sing Who died and rose on high; Who
To Thee be end - less praise, For Thou for us hast died; Be

hail Him as Thy match-less King Thro' all e - ter - ni - ty.
down - ward bends his wond'ring eye At mys - ter - ies so bright
died e - ter - nal life to bring, And lives, that death may die.
Thou, O Lord, thro' end - less days A - dored and mag - ni - fied.

248 I LOVE TO TELL THE STORY

Katherine Hankey

William G. Fischer

1. I love to tell the sto - ry Of un - seen things a - bove, Of Je - sus
2. I love to tell the sto - ry; More won - der - ful it seems Than all the
3. I love to tell the sto - ry; 'Tis pleas-ant to re - peat What seems each
4. I love to tell the sto - ry; For those who know it best Seem hun - ger-

and His glo - ry, Of Je - sus and His love, I love to tell the sto - ry,
gold - en fan-cies Of all our golden dreams. I love to tell the sto - ry,
time I tell it, More won-der-ful-ly sweet. I love to tell the sto - ry;
ing and thirsting To hear it like the rest. And when, in scenes of glo - ry,

Because I know 'tis true, It sat - is - fies my longings, As nothing else can do.
It did so much for me; And that is just the rea - son I tell it now to thee
For some have never heard The message of salvation From God's own holy word.
I sing the new, new song, 'Twill be the old, old story, That I have loved so long.

CHORUS

I love to tell the sto - ry! 'Twill be my theme in glo - ry

To tell the old, old sto - ry Of Je - sus and His love.

PRAISE HIM! PRAISE HIM!

FANNY J. CROSBY

CHESTER G. ALLEN

1. Praise Him! praise Him! Je-sus, our bless-ed Re-deem-er! Sing, O Earth, His
2. Praise Him! praise Him! Je-sus, our bless-ed Re-deem-er! For our sins He
3. Praise Him! praise Him! Je-sus, our bless-ed Re-deem-er! Heav'nly por-tals

won-der-ful love pro-claim! Hail Him! hail Him! highest archangels in glo-ry;
suffered, and bled, and died; He our Rock, our hope of e-ter-nal sal-va-tion,
loud with ho-san-nas ring! Je - sus, Sav-iour, reigneth for-ev-er and ev-er;

Strength and hon-or give to His ho-ly name! Like a shep-herd, Je-sus will
Hail Him! hail Him! Je-sus the Cru-ci-fied. Sound His Praises! Je-sus who
Crown Him! crown Him! Prophet, and Priest, and King! Christ is com-ing! o-ver the

REFRAIN

guard His children, In His arms He carries them all day long: Praise Him! praise Him!
bore our sorrows, Love unbounded, wonderful, deep and strong: Praise Him! praise Him!
world vic-to-rious, Pow'r and glo-ry un-to the Lord be-long:

tell of His ex-cel-lent greatness; Praise Him! praise Him! ev-er in joy-ful song!

250 · WHEN I'M WITH HIM

A. H. A.

COPYRIGHT, 1939, BY THE RODEHEAVER CO.
INTERNATIONAL COPYRIGHT SECURED

Rev. A. H. Ackley

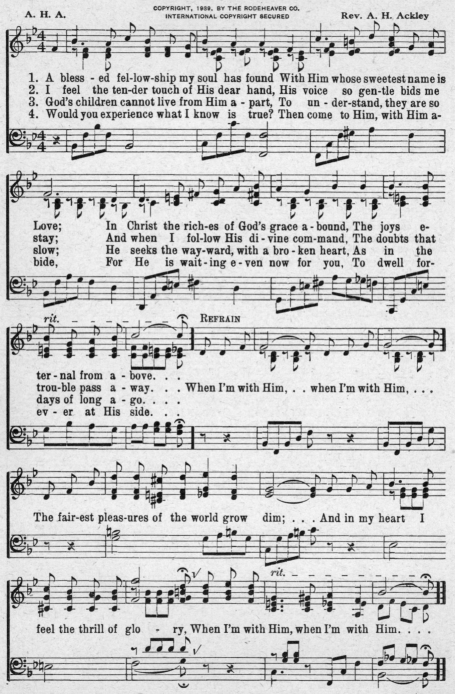

1. A bless - ed fel-low-ship my soul has found With Him whose sweetest name is
2. I feel the ten-der touch of His dear hand, His voice so gen-tle bids me
3. God's children cannot live from Him a - part, To un - der-stand, they are so
4. Would you experience what I know is true? Then come to Him, with Him a-

Love; In Christ the rich-es of God's grace a - bound, The joys e-
stay; And when I fol-low His di - vine com-mand, The doubts that
slow; He seeks the way-ward, with a bro - ken heart, As in the
bide, For He is wait-ing e - ven now for you, To dwell for-

rit. REFRAIN

ter - nal from a - bove. . . When I'm with Him, . . when I'm with Him, . . .
trou-ble pass a - way. . .
days of long a - go. . . .
ev - er at His side. . .

The fair-est pleas-ures of the world grow dim; . . . And in my heart I

rit.

feel the thrill of glo - ry, When I'm with Him, when I'm with Him. . . .

COME, YE THANKFUL PEOPLE

HENRY ALFORD

GEORGE J. ELVEY

1. Come, ye thank-ful peo-ple, come, Raise the song of har-vest-home:
2. All the world is God's own field, Fruit un-to His praise to yield;
3. For the Lord our God shall come, And shall take His har-vest home;
4. E - ven so, Lord, quick-ly come To Thy fi - nal har-vest-home;

All is safe - ly gath - ered in, Ere the win - ter storms be - gin;
Wheat and tares to - geth - er sown, Un - to joy or sor - row grown;
From His field shall in that day All of - fens - es purge a - way;
Gath - er Thou Thy peo - ple in, Free from sor - row, free from sin;

God, our Ma - ker, doth pro - vide For our wants to be sup - plied:
First the blade, and then the ear, Then the full corn shall ap - pear:
Give His an - gels charge at last In the fire the tares to cast;
There, for - ev - er pu - ri - fied, In Thy pres-ence to a - bide:

Come to God's own tem - ple, come, Raise the song of har - vest-home.
Lord of har - vest, grant that we Wholesome grain and pure may be.
But the fruit - ful ears to store In His gar - ner ev - er - more.
Come, with all Thine an - gels, come, Raise the glo-rious har - vest-home.

252 OPEN MY EYES THAT I MAY SEE

C. H. S.

CHAS. H. SCOTT

1. O-pen my eyes, that I may see, Glimpses of truth Thou hast for me;
2. O-pen my ears, that I may hear, Voi-ces of truth Thou send-est clear;
3. O-pen my mouth and let me bear Glad-ly the warm truth ev-'ry-where;

Place in my hands the won-der-ful key That shall unclasp, and set me free.
And while the wave-notes fall on my ear, Ev-'ry-thing false will dis-ap-pear.
O-pen my heart and let me prepare Love with Thy chil-dren thus to share.

Si-lent-ly now I wait for Thee, Read-y, my God, Thy will to see;
Si-lent-ly now I wait for Thee, Read-y, my God, Thy will to see;
Si-lent-ly now I wait for Thee, Read-y, my God, Thy will to see;

O-pen my eyes, il-lu-mine me, Spir-it di-vine!
O-pen my ears, il-lu-mine me, Spir-it di-vine!
O-pen my heart, il-lu-mine me, Spir-it di-vine! A-men.

253 O THAT WILL BE GLORY

C. H. G. Words and music CHAS. H. GABRIEL

1. When all my la-bors and tri-als are o'er, And I am safe on that
2. When, by the gift of His in-fi-nite grace, I am ac-cord-ed in
3. Friends will be there I have loved long a-go; Joy like a riv-er a-

beau-ti-ful shore, Just to be near the dear Lord I a-dore,
heav-en a place, Just to be there and to look on His face,
round me will flow; Yet, just a smile from my Sav-iour, I know,

rit. CHORUS. *Faster.*

Will thro' the a-ges be glo-ry for me.... O that will be
O............... that will

glo-ry for me, Glo-ry for me, glo-ry for me; When by His grace
be glo-ry for me, glo-ry for me, glo-ry for me;...........

rit.

I shall look on His face, That will be glo-ry, be glo-ry for me.

SAVED TO THE UTTERMOST

"He is able also to save them to the uttermost that come unto God by Him."—HEB. 7: 25]

W. J. K.

W. J. KIRKPATRICK

1. Saved to the ut - ter-most: I am the Lord's Je - sus, my
2. Saved to the ut - ter-most: Je - sus is near; Keep - ing me
3. Saved to the ut - ter-most: this I can say, "Once all was
4. Saved to the ut - ter-most; cheer-ful - ly sing Loud hal - le -

Sav - iour, sal - va - tion af - fords; Gives me His Spir - it, a
safe - ly, He cast - eth out fear; Trust - ing His prom - is - es,
dark - ness, but now it is day; Beau - ti - ful vis - ions of
lu - ias to Je - sus, my King; Ran-somed and par - doned, re -

wit - ness with - in, Whisp'ring of par - don, and sav - ing from sin.
now I am blest; Lean - ing up - on Him, how sweet is my rest.
glo - ry I see, Je - sus in bright-ness re - vealed un - to me."
deemed by His blood, Cleansed from un - right-eous-ness; glo - ry to God!

REFRAIN

Saved, saved, saved to the ut - ter-most, Saved, saved by pow - er di - vine;

Saved, saved, saved to the ut - ter-most: Je - sus, the Sav-iour is mine!

MOTHER'S PRAYERS HAVE FOLLOWED ME

Lizzie DeArmond.

B. D. Ackley

1. I grieved my Lord from day to day, I scorned His love so full and free, And though I wan-dered far a-way, My moth-er's
2. O'er des-ert wild, o'er mountain high A wan-der-er I chose to be, A wretch-ed soul con-demned to die, Still moth-er's
3. He turned my dark-ness in-to light, This bless-ed Christ of Cal-va-ry, I'll praise His name both day and night, That moth-er's

REFRAIN.

pray'rs have fol-lowed me. I'm com-ing home, I'm com-ing home, To live my wast-ed life a-new, For moth-er's pray'rs have fol-lowed me, Have fol-lowed me the whole world thro'.

256 IT IS WELL WITH MY SOUL

H. G. Spafford

P. P. Bliss

1. When peace, like a riv-er, at-tend-eth my way, When sor-rows like
2. Though Sa-tan should buf-fet, tho' tri-als should come, Let this blest as-
3. My sin— oh, the bliss of this glo-ri-ous tho't—My sin—not in
4. And, Lord, haste the day when the faith shall be sight, The clouds be rolled

sea-bil-lows roll; What-ev-er my lot, Thou hast taught me to say,
sur-ance con-trol, That Christ has re-gard-ed my help-less es-tate,
part, but the whole, Is nailed to the cross and I bear it no more,
back as a scroll, The trump shall re-sound and the Lord shall de-scend,

CHORUS

It is well, it is well with my soul.
And hath shed His own blood for my soul. It is well.....with my
Praise the Lord, praise the Lord, O my soul!
"E-ven so"—it is well with my soul. It is well

soul,...... It is well, it is well with my soul.
with my soul,

257   TELL IT TO JESUS

J. E. Rankin, D. D.
E. S. Lorenz

1. Are you wea - ry, are you heav - y - heart - ed? Tell it to Je - sus,
2. Do the tears flow down your cheeks un - bid - den? Tell it to Je - sus,
3. Do you fear the gath - 'ring clouds of sor - row? Tell it to Je - sus,
4. Are you troub - led at the tho't of dy - ing? Tell it to Je - sus,

Tell it to Je - sus; Are you griev - ing o - ver joys de - part - ed?
Tell it to Je - sus; Have you sins that to men's eyes are hid - den?
Tell it to Je - sus; Are you anx - ious what shall be to - mor - row?
Tell it to Je - sus; For Christ's com - ing King - dom are you sigh - ing?

CHORUS

Tell it to Je - sus a - lone. Tell it to Je - sus, Tell it to Je - sus,

He is a friend that's well - known; You've no oth - er

such a friend or broth - er, Tell it to Je - sus a - lone.

Sir Robert Grant   **Francis Joseph Haydn**

1. O wor-ship the King, all - glo-rious a - bove, And grate-ful-ly
2. O tell of His might, and sing of His grace, Whose robe is the
3. Thy boun-ti-ful care what tongue can re - cite? It breathes in the
4. Frail chil-dren of dust, and fee-ble as frail, In Thee do we

sing His won-der-ful love; Our Shield and De-fend-er, the An-cient of
light, whose can-o-py space; His char-iots of wrath the deep thun-der-clouds
air, it shines in the light; It streams from the hills, it de-scends to the
trust, nor find Thee to fail; Thy mer-cies how ten-der! how firm to the

days, Pa - vil-ioned in splen-dor, and gird - ed with praise.
form, And dark is His path on the wings of the storm.
plain, And sweet-ly dis - tills in the dew and the rain.
end! Our Mak-er, De-fend-er, Re - deem-er, and Friend. A - MEN.

259 JESUS, THE VERY THOUGHT OF THEE

Bernard of Clairvaux
Trans. by Edward Caswall   **John B. Dykes**

1. Je - sus, the ver - y thought of Thee With sweetness fills the breast;
2. Nor voice can sing, nor heart can frame, Nor can the mem - 'ry find
3. O Hope of ev - 'ry con - trite heart, O Joy of all the meek,
4. But what to those who find? Ah, this Nor tongue nor pen can show:
5. Je - sus, our on - ly joy be Thou, As Thou our prize wilt be;

But sweet-er far Thy face to see, And in Thy pres-ence rest.
A sweet-er sound than Thy blest name, O Sav-ior of man-kind!
To those who ask, how kind Thou art! How good to those who seek!
The love of Je-sus, what it is, None but His loved ones know.
In Thee be all our glo-ry now, And thru e-ter-ni-ty. A-MEN.

260 HAVE THINE OWN WAY, LORD

A. A. P.

COPYRIGHT, 1935, RENEWAL
HOPE PUBLISHING CO., OWNER

Geo. C. Stebbins

Slowly

1. Have Thine own way, Lord! Have Thine own way! Thou art the
2. Have Thine own way, Lord! Have Thine own way! Search me and
3. Have Thine own way, Lord! Have Thine own way! Wound-ed and
4. Have Thine own way, Lord! Have Thine own way! Hold o'er my

Pot-ter; I am the clay Mould me and make me Aft-er Thy
try me, Mas-ter, to-day! Whit-er than snow, Lord, Wash me just
wea-ry, Help me, I pray! Pow-er—all pow-er—Sure-ly is
be-ing Ab-so-lute sway! Fill with Thy Spir-it Till all shall

will, While I am wait-ing, Yield-ed and still.
now, As in Thy pres-ence Hum-bly I bow.
Thine! Touch me and heal me, Sav-iour di-vine!
see. Christ on-ly, al-ways, Liv-ing in me!

THE NAME OF JESUS

261

W. C. Martin

E. S. LORENZ

1. The name of Je - sus is so sweet, I love its mu - sic
2. I love the name of Him whose heart Knows all my griefs and
3. That name I fond - ly love to hear, It nev - er fails my
4. No word of man can ev - er tell How sweet the name I

to re - peat; It makes my joys full and com - plete, The pre - cious
bears a part; Who bids all an - xious fears de - part— I love the
heart to cheer, Its mu - sic dries the fall - ing tear; Ex - alt the
love so well, Oh, let its prais - es ev - er swell, Oh, praise the

CHORUS

name of Je - sus. "Je - sus," oh, how sweet the name!
pre - cious name,

"Je - sus," ev - 'ry day the same; "Je - sus," let all

saints pro - claim its wor - thy praise for - ev - er.
Its wor - thy praise

262 GOD WILL TAKE CARE OF YOU

(Dedicated to my wife, Mrs. John A. Davis)

C. D. MARTIN   W. S. MARTIN

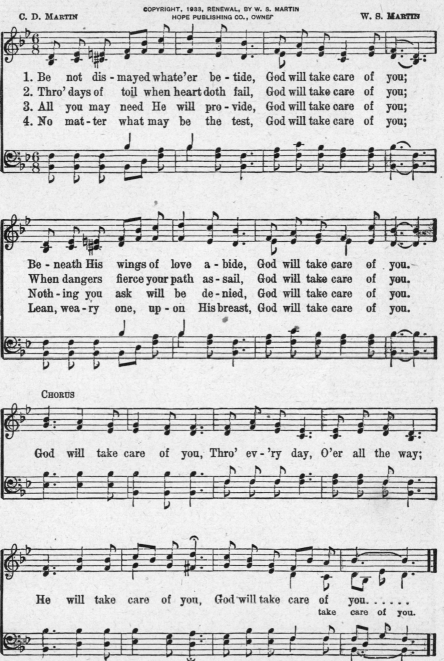

1. Be not dis-mayed whate'er be-tide, God will take care of you;
2. Thro' days of toil when heart doth fail, God will take care of you;
3. All you may need He will pro-vide, God will take care of you;
4. No mat-ter what may be the test, God will take care of you;

Be-neath His wings of love a-bide, God will take care of you.
When dangers fierce your path as-sail, God will take care of you.
Noth-ing you ask will be de-nied, God will take care of you.
Lean, wea-ry one, up-on His breast, God will take care of you.

CHORUS

God will take care of you, Thro' ev-'ry day, O'er all the way;

He will take care of you, God will take care of you.......
take care of you.

263 I'LL GO WHERE YOU WANT ME TO GO

MARY BROWN

CARRIE E. ROUNSEFELL

I'LL GO WHERE YOU WANT ME TO GO

I'll say what you want me to say, dear Lord, I'll be what you want me to be.

264   **TRANSFORMED**

MRS. F. G. BURROUGHS   B. D. ACKLEY

1. Dear Lord, take up my tan-gled strands, Where we have wrought in vain,
2. Touch Thou the sad, dis-cord-ant keys Of ev-'ry troub-led breast,
3. Where bro-ken vows in frag-ments lie The toll of wast-ed years,
4. Take all the fail-ures, each mis-take Of our poor, hu-man ways,

That by the skill of Thy dear hands Some beau-ty may re-main.
And change to peace-ful har-mo-nies The sigh-ings of un-rest.
Do Thou make whole a-gain, we cry, And give a song for tears.
Then, Sav-iour, for Thine own dear sake, Make them show forth Thy praise.

CHORUS

Transformed by grace di-vine, The glo-ry shall be Thine;
Trans-formed   The glo-ry

To Thy most ho-ly will, O Lord, We now our all re-sign.

265 I AM COMING HOME

A. H. ACKLEY

B. D. ACKLEY

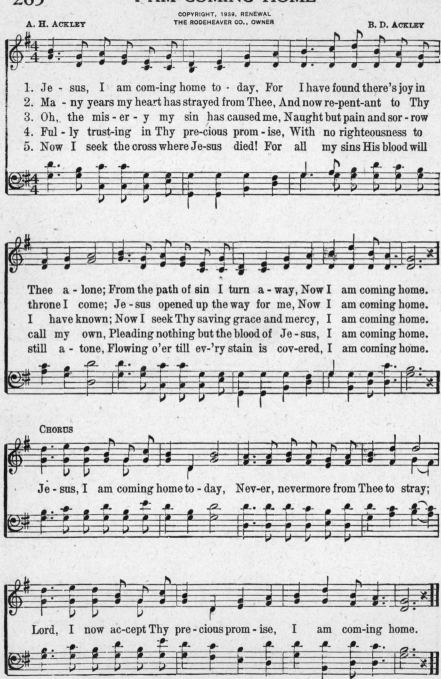

1. Je - sus, I am com-ing home to - day, For I have found there's joy in
2. Ma - ny years my heart has strayed from Thee, And now re-pent-ant to Thy
3. Oh, the mis - er - y my sin has caused me, Naught but pain and sor - row
4. Ful - ly trust-ing in Thy pre-cious prom - ise, With no righteousness to
5. Now I seek the cross where Je-sus died! For all my sins His blood will

Thee a - lone; From the path of sin I turn a - way, Now I am coming home.
throne I come; Je - sus opened up the way for me, Now I am coming home.
I have known; Now I seek Thy saving grace and mercy, I am coming home.
call my own, Pleading nothing but the blood of Je - sus, I am coming home.
still a - tone, Flowing o'er till ev-'ry stain is cov-ered, I am coming home.

CHORUS

Je - sus, I am coming home to - day, Nev-er, nevermore from Thee to stray;

Lord, I now ac-cept Thy pre-cious prom - ise, I am com-ing home.

266 GOD'S WAY

Lida Shivers Leech

Lida Shivers Leech

DUET. *Espressivo*

1. God's way is the best way, Tho' I may not see Why sor-rows and
2. God's way is the best way, My path He hath planned, I'll trust in Him
3. God's way shall be my way, He know-eth the best, And lean-ing up-

tri-als Oft gath-er 'round me; He ev-er is seek-ing
al-way While hold-ing His hand. In shad-ow or sun-shine
on Him, Sweet, sweet is my rest. No harm can be-fall me,

My gold to re-fine, So hum-bly I trust Him, My Sav-ior di-vine.
He ev-er is near, With Him for my ref-uge, I nev-er need fear.
Safe, safe shall I be, I'll cling to Him ev-er, So pre-cious is He.

CHORUS *Animato*

God's way is the best way, God's way is the right way,

rit.

I'll trust in Him al-way, He know-eth the best.

267 AT THE CROSS

ISAAC WATTS   R. E. HUDSON

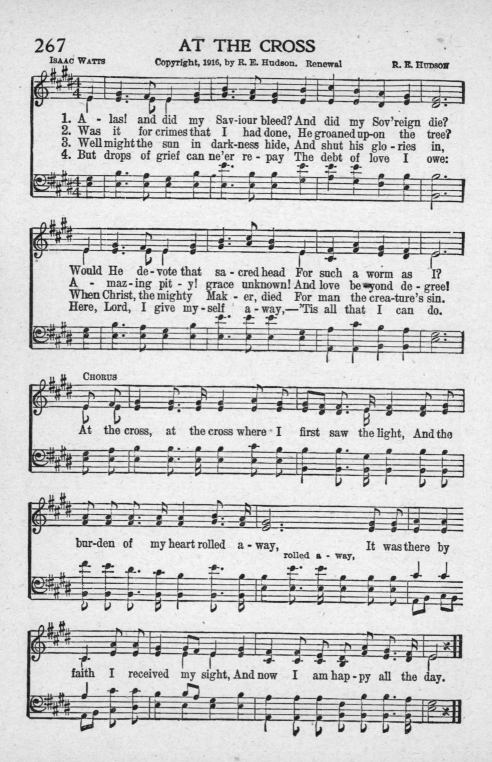

1. A - las! and did my Sav-iour bleed? And did my Sov'reign die?
2. Was it for crimes that I had done, He groaned up-on the tree?
3. Well might the sun in dark-ness hide, And shut his glo - ries in,
4. But drops of grief can ne'er re - pay The debt of love I owe:

Would He de - vote that sa - cred head For such a worm as I?
A - maz-ing pit - y! grace unknown! And love be-yond de - gree!
When Christ, the mighty Mak - er, died For man the crea-ture's sin.
Here, Lord, I give my-self a - way,—'Tis all that I can do.

CHORUS

At the cross, at the cross where I first saw the light, And the
bur-den of my heart rolled a - way,
rolled a - way,
It was there by
faith I received my sight, And now I am hap - py all the day.

HIGHER GROUND

Johnson Oatman, Jr. Chas. H. Gabriel

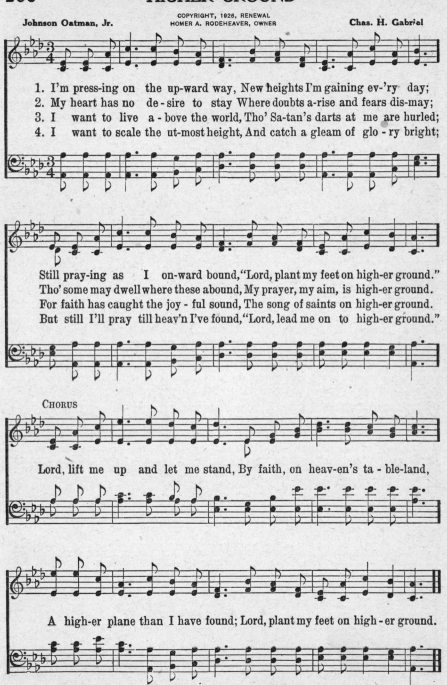

1. I'm press-ing on the up-ward way, New heights I'm gaining ev-'ry day;
2. My heart has no de-sire to stay Where doubts a-rise and fears dis-may;
3. I want to live a-bove the world, Tho' Sa-tan's darts at me are hurled;
4. I want to scale the ut-most height, And catch a gleam of glo-ry bright;

Still pray-ing as I on-ward bound, "Lord, plant my feet on high-er ground."
Tho' some may dwell where these abound, My prayer, my aim, is high-er ground.
For faith has caught the joy-ful sound, The song of saints on high-er ground.
But still I'll pray till heav'n I've found, "Lord, lead me on to high-er ground."

CHORUS

Lord, lift me up and let me stand, By faith, on heav-en's ta-ble-land,

A high-er plane than I have found; Lord, plant my feet on high-er ground.

269 TELL ME THE STORY OF JESUS

Fanny J. Crosby

Jno. R. Sweney

1. Tell me the sto-ry of Je-sus, Write on my heart ev-'ry word;
2. Fast-ing a-lone in the des-ert, Tell of the days that are past,
3. Tell of the cross where they nailed Him, Writh-ing in an-guish and pain;

CHO.—*Tell me the sto-ry of Je-sus, Write on my heart ev-'ry word;*

FINE

Tell me the sto-ry most pre-cious, Sweet-est that ev-er was heard.
How for our sins He was tempt-ed, Yet was tri-um-phant at last.
Tell of the grave where they laid Him, Tell how He liv-eth a-gain.

Tell me the sto-ry most pre-cious, Sweet-est that ev-er was heard.

Tell how the an-gels, in cho-rus, Sang as they welcomed His birth,
Tell of the years of His la-bor, Tell of the sor-row He bore,
Love in that sto-ry so ten-der, Clear-er than ev-er I see:

D. C. for Chorus

"Glo-ry to God in the high-est! Peace and good ti-dings to earth."
He was de-spised and af-flict-ed, Home-less, re-ject-ed and poor.
Stay, let me weep while you whis-per, Love paid the ran-som for me.

270 THE HAVEN OF REST.

H. L. GILMOUR   Used by per. Dr. H. L. Gilmour   GEORGE D. MOORE

1. My soul in sad ex-ile was out on life's sea, So burdened with
2. I yield-ed my-self to His ten-der em-brace, And faith tak-ing
3. The song of my soul, since the Lord made me whole, Has been the old
4. How pre-cious the tho't that we all may re-cline, Like John the be-
5. O come to the Sav-iour, He pa-tient-ly waits To save by His

sin and dis-tressed, Till I heard a sweet voice saying, "Make me your choice;"
hold of the Word, My fet-ters fell off, and I an-chored my soul;
sto-ry so blest, Of Je-sus who'll save who-so-ev-er will have
lov-ed and blest, On Je-sus' strong arm, where no tem-pest can harm,
pow-er di-vine; Come, an-chor your soul in the "Ha-ven of Rest,"

CHORUS

And I entered the "Ha-ven of Rest."
The "Ha-ven of Rest" is my Lord.
A home in the "Ha-ven of Rest." I've anchored my soul in the
Se-cure in the "Ha-ven of Rest."
And say, "My Be-lov-ed is mine."

"Ha-ven of Rest," I'll sail the wide seas no more; The tempest may

sweep o'er the wild storm-y deep; In Je-sus I'm safe ev-er-more.

271

ONLY SHADOWS.

A. H. A.

A. H. Ackley.

1. There are shadows of sor-row that dark-en life's way, They are on-ly
2. There are shadows of fear bringing tho'ts that dis-may, They are on-ly
3. There are shadows of doubt that steal in-to our mind, They are on-ly
4. There are shadows of death that are black with despair, They are on-ly

shad-ows, But be-hind the dark shad-ows shines love's kind-ly ray,
shad-ows, If we walk in His love they will all pass a-way,
shad-ows, If we look to the cross blest as-sur-ance we find,
shad-ows, For Christ Je-sus, the Light of the world, will be there,

Chorus.

They are on-ly shad-ows. Do not doubt, do not fear, When the

shadows ap-pear, Just re-mem-ber that dark lone-ly shad-ows Can-not

hide God's dear face, If we trust in His grace, They are on-ly shad-ows.

272 SOFTLY AND TENDERLY

HOPE PUB. CO., OWNERS

W. L. T.

WILL L. THOMPSON

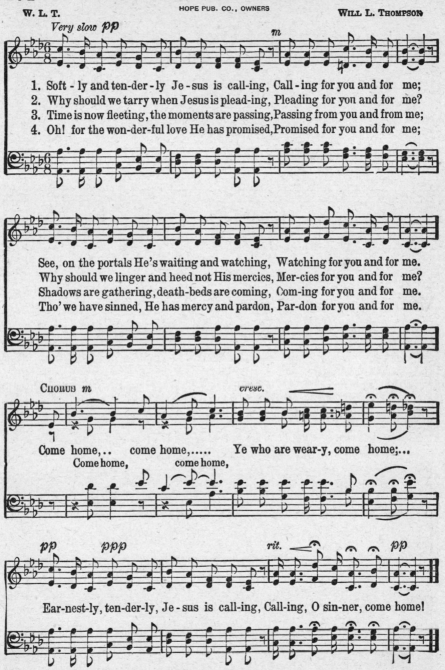

1. Soft - ly and ten-der - ly Je - sus is call-ing, Call - ing for you and for me;
2. Why should we tarry when Jesus is plead-ing, Pleading for you and for me?
3. Time is now fleeting, the moments are passing, Passing from you and from me;
4. Oh! for the won-der-ful love He has promised, Promised for you and for me;

See, on the portals He's waiting and watching, Watching for you and for me.
Why should we linger and heed not His mercies, Mer-cies for you and for me?
Shadows are gathering, death-beds are coming, Com-ing for you and for me.
Tho' we have sinned, He has mercy and pardon, Par-don for you and for me.

Come home,.. come home,...... Ye who are wear-y, come home;...
Come home, come home,

Ear-nest-ly, ten-der-ly, Je-sus is call-ing, Call-ing, O sin-ner, come home!

SOUND THE BATTLE CRY

W. F. S.

WM. F. SHERWIN

1. Sound the bat-tle cry! See, the foe is nigh; Raise the standard high
2. Strong to meet the foe, Marching on we go, While our cause we know,
3. O Thou God of all, Hear us when we call, Help us one and all

For the Lord; Gird your ar-mor on, Stand firm, ev-'ry one; Rest your
Must pre-vail; Shield and banner bright, Gleam-ing in the light; Bat-tling
By Thy grace; When the bat-tle's done, And the vic-t'ry's won, May we

Chorus ff

cause up-on His ho-ly word.
for the right We ne'er can fail. Rouse, then, sol-diers, ral-ly round the
wear the crown Be-fore Thy face.

ban-ner, Read-y, stead-y, pass the word a-long; On-ward, for-ward,

shout a-loud Ho-san-na! Christ is Cap-tain of the might-y throng.

274 WE'RE MARCHING TO ZION

ISAAC WATTS   COPYRIGHT PROPERTY OF MARY RUNYAN LOWRY.   USED BY PERMISSION   ROBERT LOWRY

Spirited

1. Come, we that love the Lord, And let our joys be known, Join
2. Let those re - fuse to sing Who nev - er knew our God; But
3. The hill of Zi - on yields A thou-sand sa - cred sweets Be -
4. Then let our songs abound, And ev - 'ry tear be dry; We're

in a song with sweet ac-cord, Join in a song with sweet accord, And
chil-dren of the heav'n-ly King, But chil-dren of the heav'nly King, May
fore we reach the heav'n-ly fields, Be-fore we reach the heav'nly fields, Or
marching thro' Immanuel's ground, We're marching thro' Immanuel's ground, To

thus sur - round the throne, And thus sur-round the throne.
speak their joys a - broad, May speak their joys a - broad.
walk the gold - en streets, Or walk the gold - en streets.
fair - er worlds on high, To fair - er worlds on high.

thus sur - round the throne, And thus sur - round the throne.

CHORUS

We're march - ing to Zi - on, Beau-ti - ful, beau-ti-ful Zi - on; We're
We're marching on to Zi - on,

march-ing upward to Zi - on, The beau-ti-ful cit-y of God.
Zi - on, Zi - on,

275 THE KINGDOM IS COMING

MARY B. C. SLADE

ROBERT M. McINTOSH

1. From all the dark pla - ces Of earth's hea-then ra - ces, O
2. The sun - light is glanc - ing O'er ar - mies ad - vanc - ing To
3. With shout - ing and sing - ing, And ju - bi-lant ring - ing, Their

see how the thick shadows fly! The voice of sal - va - tion A -
con - quer the king - doms of sin; Our Lord shall pos-sess them, His
arms of re - bel - lion cast down, At last ev - 'ry na - tion, The

wakes ev - 'ry na - tion, "Come o - ver and help us," they cry.
pres - ence shall bless them, His beau - ty shall en - ter them in.
Lord of sal - va - tion Their King and Re - deem - er shall crown!

REFRAIN

The kingdom is coming, O tell ye the story, God's banner ex-alt-ed shall be!

The earth shall be full of His knowledge and glory, As waters that cover the sea!

BENEATH THE CROSS OF JESUS

Elizabeth C. Clephane

Frederick C. Maker

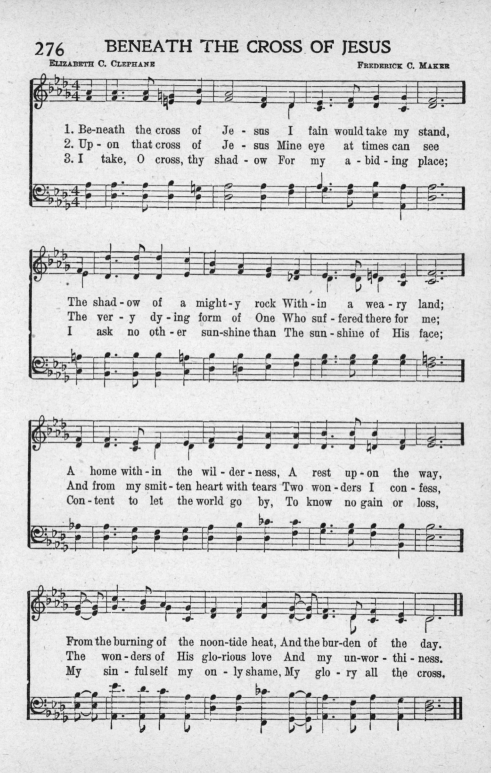

1. Be-neath the cross of Je-sus I fain would take my stand,
2. Up-on that cross of Je-sus Mine eye at times can see
3. I take, O cross, thy shad-ow For my a-bid-ing place;

The shad-ow of a might-y rock With-in a wea-ry land;
The ver-y dy-ing form of One Who suf-fered there for me;
I ask no oth-er sun-shine than The sun-shine of His face;

A home with-in the wil-der-ness, A rest up-on the way,
And from my smit-ten heart with tears Two won-ders I con-fess,
Con-tent to let the world go by, To know no gain or loss,

From the burning of the noon-tide heat, And the bur-den of the day.
The won-ders of His glo-rious love And my un-wor-thi-ness.
My sin-ful self my on-ly shame, My glo-ry all the cross.

277 GLORIOUS THINGS OF THEE ARE SPOKEN

John Newton   AUSTRIA 8. 7. 8. 7. D.   Francis J. Haydn

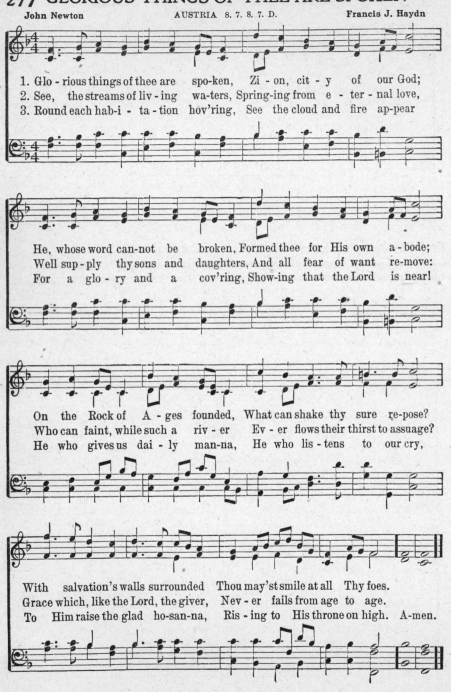

1. Glo - rious things of thee are spo-ken, Zi - on, cit - y of our God;
2. See, the streams of liv - ing wa-ters, Spring-ing from e - ter - nal love,
3. Round each hab-i - ta - tion hov'ring, See the cloud and fire ap-pear

He, whose word can-not be broken, Formed thee for His own a - bode;
Well sup - ply thy sons and daughters, And all fear of want re-move:
For a glo - ry and a cov'ring, Show-ing that the Lord is near!

On the Rock of A - ges founded, What can shake thy sure re-pose?
Who can faint, while such a riv - er Ev - er flows their thirst to assuage?
He who gives us dai - ly man-na, He who lis - tens to our cry,

With salvation's walls surrounded Thou may'st smile at all Thy foes.
Grace which, like the Lord, the giver, Nev - er fails from age to age.
To Him raise the glad ho-san-na, Ris - ing to His throne on high. A-men.

JESUS, LOVER OF MY SOUL

ABERYSTWYTH

Charles Wesley

J. Parry, Mus. Doc.

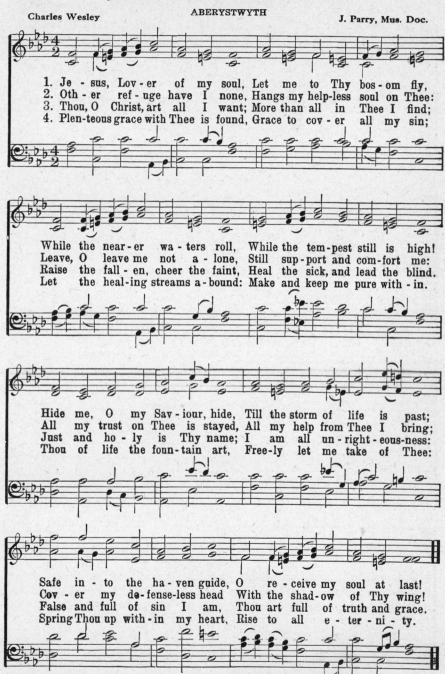

1. Je - sus, Lov - er of my soul, Let me to Thy bos - om fly,
2. Oth - er ref - uge have I none, Hangs my help-less soul on Thee:
3. Thou, O Christ, art all I want; More than all in Thee I find;
4. Plen-teous grace with Thee is found, Grace to cov - er all my sin;

While the near - er wa - ters roll, While the tem-pest still is high!
Leave, O leave me not a - lone, Still sup-port and com-fort me:
Raise the fall - en, cheer the faint, Heal the sick, and lead the blind.
Let the heal-ing streams a-bound: Make and keep me pure with - in.

Hide me, O my Sav - iour, hide, Till the storm of life is past;
All my trust on Thee is stayed, All my help from Thee I bring;
Just and ho - ly is Thy name; I am all un - right - eous-ness:
Thou of life the foun - tain art, Free-ly let me take of Thee:

Safe in - to the ha - ven guide, O re - ceive my soul at last!
Cov - er my de-fense-less head With the shad-ow of Thy wing!
False and full of sin I am, Thou art full of truth and grace.
Spring Thou up with-in my heart, Rise to all e - ter-ni - ty.

279 ALL HAIL, IMMANUEL!

D. R. VAN SICKLE

CHAS. H. GABRIEL

1. All hail to Thee, Im-man-u-el, We cast . . . our crowns be-fore Thee;
2. All hail to Thee, Im-man-u-el, The ran - somed hosts surround Thee;
3. All hail to Thee, Im-man-u-el, Our ris - - en King and Sav-iour!

Let ev - 'ry heart o - bey Thy will, And ev - - - 'ry voice a-
And earth - ly mon-archs clam - or forth Their Sov - - 'reign King to
Thy foes are van-quished, and Thou art Om - nip - - o - tent for-

dore Thee. In praise to Thee, our Sav - ior King, The vi - brant
crown Thee. While those re-deemed in a - ges gone, As - sem - bled
ev - er. Death, sin and hell no lon - ger reign, And Sa - tan's

chords of Heav - en ring, And ech - o back the might - y strain:
round the great white throne, Break forth in - to im - mor - tal song:
pow'r is burst in twain; E - ter - nal glo - ry to Thy Name:

All hail! all hail! All hail! all hail! Im-man-u - el!
All hail! all hail!

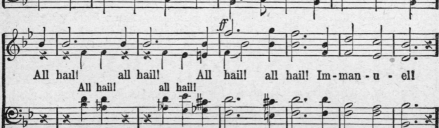

ALL HAIL, IMMANUEL!

CHORUS.

Hail! . . . . . . Im-man-u-el! Im-man-u-el! Hail! . . . . . .

Hail to the King we love so well! Hail! Im-man-u-el! Hail to the King we love so well!

Hail! . . . . .

Im-man-u-el! Im-man-u-el!

Hail! Im-man-u-el! Glo-ry and honor and majesty, Wisdom and power be
Hail! . . . . Glo - - ry and maj-es-ty, Wis - dom be

rit. . . . . Hail! . . . . . Im-

un - to Thee, Now and ev - er - more! . . . Hail to the King we love so well!

man-u-el! Im-man-u-el! Hail! . . . . . . Im-man-u-el! Im-man-u-el!

Hail! Im - man-u-el! Hail to the King we love so well! Hail! Im - man-u - el!
Hail! . . . . . . Hail! . . . . . .

King of kings and Lord of lords, All hail, Im-man-u - el! A-MEN.

ALL HAIL THE POWER OF JESUS' NAME

DIADEM. C. M.

Edward Perronet

James Ellor

1. All hail the power of Je - sus' name! Let an - gels prostrate fall,
2. Ye cho - sen seed of Is - rael's race, Ye ran-somed from the fall,
3. Let ev - 'ry kin - dred, ev - 'ry tribe, On this ter - res - trial ball,
4. O that with yon - der sa - cred throng We at His feet may fall,

Let an - gels pros-trate fall; Bring forth the roy - al di - a - dem,
Ye ran-somed from the fall, Hail Him who saves you by His grace,
On this ter - res - trial ball, To Him all maj - es - ty as - cribe,
We at His feet may fall! We'll join the ev - er - last - ing song,

And crown . . . . Him, Crown Him,
And crown Him, crown Him, crown Him, crown Him, And crown Him Lord of
And crown . . . . Him, Crown Him,

And crown Him, crown Him, crown Him, Crown . . . .

crown Him, crown Him;

all, crown Him; And crown Him Lord of all! A-MEN.
crown . . . . Him;

. . . . Him; And crown Him Lord of all!

SAIL ON!

281

C. H. G.

Chas. H. Gabriel.

1. Up - on a wide and stormy sea, Thou'rt sail-ing to e - ter - ni - ty,
2. Art far from shore, and wea-ry-worn—The sky o'er-cast, the can-vas torn?
3. Do comrades trem - ble and re - fuse To fur - ther dare the taunting hues?
4. Do snarling waves thy craft as - sail? Art pow'rless, drift-ing with the gale?

Ad lib.

And thy great Ad-m'ral or-ders Thee:—"Sail on! sail on! sail on!"
Hark ye! a voice to thee is borne:—"Sail on! sail on! sail on!"
No oth - er course is thine to choose, Sail on! sail on! sail on!
Take heart! God's word shall nev - er fail! Sail on! sail on! sail on!

CHORUS.

Sail on! sail on! the storms will soon be past, The dark - ness will not al - ways last; Sail on! sail on! . . . . . . God

Sail on! sail on!

lives! and He commands:"Sail on! sail on!" . . . .

Rit. e dim *pp*

on! sail on! sail on sail on!

* May close here.

282 THOU MIGHTY TO SAVE

Fanny J. Crosby

Chas. H. Gabriel

INTRODUCTION

1. O Je - sus, my Lord and Sav-iour, Who gav-est Thy life for
2. The world like a dream will van-ish, The hope like the years de-
3. O what are the toils and la-bors, The cross-es that now I

me, ... No room in my heart for pleas-ures That
cay, ... Its beau - ties like dew - y blos-soms Will
bear, ... Com-pared with the crown im - mor - tal Laid

have not their trust in Thee; .... Earth has no a-
with - er and pass a - way; ..... But Thou wilt a-
up for my soul to wear? .... 'Twill mat - ter to

bid - ing cit - y,—Not here is my place of rest,— I seek for a
bide un-chang-ing, My sure de-fense wilt be; O Je - sus, my
me but lit - tle What con - flicts I have passed, If, aft - er the

THOU MIGHTY TO SAVE

bright-er coun-try, A home with the pure and blest. . . .
Lord and Sav - ior, I'm trust-ing a - lone in Thee. . . .
strife is end - ed, I rest at Thy feet at last. . . .

CHORUS

And oh, when my course is fin - ished, And vic - tor's palm I
And oh, when my course is fin-ished, And vic - tor's

wave, ... To Thee will I give the glo - ry, . . . O
palm I wave, glo - ry, O

cres.

Thou, who art might - y to save, ... To Thee will I give the
save, To Thee

ff   *slower*

glo - ry . . . . O Thou, who art might - y to save. . . .

283 AWAKENING CHORUS

Charlotte G. Homer

Chas. H. Gabriel

1. A - wake! A-wake! a - wake! A-wake! and sing the bless - ed sto - ry;
2. Ring out! Ring out! ring out! ring out! O bells of joy and glad - ness!

A-wake! A-wake! a - wake! A-wake! and let your song of praise a - rise; A-
Re-peat, Re-peat, re-peat re-peat a - new the sto - ry o'er a - gain, Till

wake! A-wake! a - wake! a-wake! the earth is full of glo - ry, And light is
all Till all the earth the earth shall lose its weight of sad-ness, And shout a-

Male voices in Unison

beam - ing from the ra-diant skies; The rocks and rills, the vales and
is beam-ing
new a-new the glo - ri - ous re - frain; With an - gels in the heights sing

hills re-sound with glad-ness, All na - ture joins to sing the tri-umph
of the great sal - va - tion He wrest - ed from the hand of sin and

AWAKENING CHORUS

Full harmony

song. The Lord Je - ho - vah reigns and sin is back-ward hurled!
death. The Lord Je - ho - vah reigns and sin is back-ward hurled!
sin is backward hurled!

Unison

Re-joice, re-joice! Lift heart and voice; Je - ho - vah reigns!

Full harmony

Pro-claim His sov-'reign pow'r to all the world, And let His
pow'r to all the world, And let the

glo - rious ban-ner be un - furled! Je - ho - vah reigns!
grand and glo-rious ban - ner be un-furled! Je - ho - vah reigns! Je - ho - vah reigns!

Re-joice! re - joice! re - joice! Je - ho - vah reigns!
Re-joice! re - joice! re - joice!

284   FILL ME NOW

E. H. Stokes, D.D.

Jno. R. Sweney

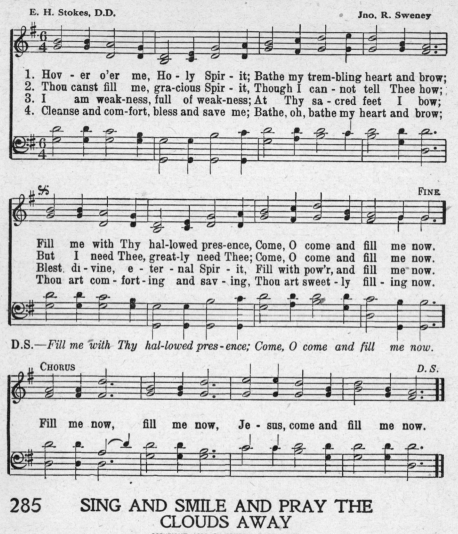

1. Hov - er o'er me, Ho - ly Spir - it; Bathe my trem-bling heart and brow;
2. Thou canst fill me, gra-cious Spir - it, Though I can-not tell Thee how;
3. I am weak-ness, full of weak-ness; At Thy sa-cred feet I bow;
4. Cleanse and com-fort, bless and save me; Bathe, oh, bathe my heart and brow;

Fill me with Thy hal-lowed pres-ence, Come, O come and fill me now.
But I need Thee, great-ly need Thee; Come, O come and fill me now.
Blest, di-vine, e-ter-nal Spir - it, Fill with pow'r, and fill me now.
Thou art com-fort-ing and sav - ing, Thou art sweet-ly fill - ing now.

D.S.—*Fill me with Thy hal-lowed pres-ence; Come, O come and fill me now.*

CHORUS

Fill me now, fill me now, Je - sus, come and fill me now.

285   SING AND SMILE AND PRAY THE CLOUDS AWAY

COPYRIGHT, 1934, BY HOMER A. RODEHEAVER
INTERNATIONAL COPYRIGHT SECURED

Written by The Brocks

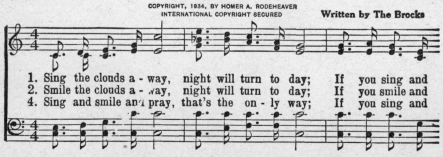

1. Sing the clouds a - way, night will turn to day; If you sing and
2. Smile the clouds a - way, night will turn to day; If you smile and
4. Sing and smile and pray, that's the on - ly way; If you sing and

FINE.

sing and sing, You'll sing the clouds a - way.
smile and smile, You'll smile the clouds a - way.   3. Pray the clouds a - way,
smile and pray, You'll drive the clouds a - way.

D. C. 4th Verse

Pray and pray and pray; Night will turn to day, No mat- ter what they say.

286   **O WHAT A WONDER**

Copyright, 1938, by The Rodeheaver Co.
International Copyright Secured

R. S.   RALPH SCHURMAN

O what a won-der that Je - sus found me, Out in the dark-ness, no

light could I see, O what a won - der, He put His great arm

And won - der of won - ders,

un - der, And won - der of won - ders, He saved ev - en me,

287 WHEN MORNING DAWNS

A. H. A.   Rev. A. H. Ackley

1. A per-fect day   is com-ing by and by,   A day of peace and
2. With-in its por - tals fade-less joys a - bide,   O what al - lur - ing
3. How lit - tle then   the trials of life will seem, How light, the heav - y
4. So trust in God, how - ev - er dark the way,   And wait with pa - tience

free-dom from all care,   With all the good   for which our spir-its
love - li - ness is found!   Be - yond the fleet - ing shad-ows that a-
bur-dens we have borne;   The deep-est   sor - row, like a pass-ing
for the morn to break;   Cling to His hand   un - til the dawn of

sigh, . . . And not a cloud to dim its sky so   fair. . . .
bide, . . . Is Christ the Lord with end-less glo - ries crowned. . . .
dream, . . . Will be for - got - ten in that bless - ed morn. . . .
day, . . . In His own like-ness we shall then a - wake. . . .

CHORUS

When morn-ing dawns, fare-well to ev - 'ry sor - row, Fare - well to

all the trou-bles of to - day, There'll be no pain, no death in God's to-

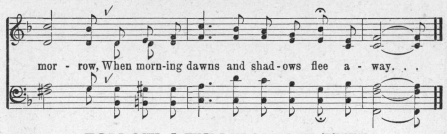

mor - row, When morn-ing dawns and shad-ows flee a - way. . .

288 FOLLOW, I WILL FOLLOW THEE

H. L. B.
Margaret W. Brown

Howard L. Brown

1. Je-sus calls me, I must fol-low, Fol-low Him to-day;   When His ten-der
2. Je-sus calls me, I must fol-low, Fol-low ev-'ry hour,   Know the bless-ing
3. Je-sus calls me, I must fol-low, Fol-low Him al-way;   When my Sav-iour

CHORUS *Slowly*

voice is plead-ing, How can I de - lay?   Fol - low, I will fol-low
of His pres-ence, Full-ness of His pow'r.
goes be - fore me I can nev-er stray.

Thee, my Lord,   Fol - low ev-'ry pass-ing day. . .   My to-

mor-rows are all known to Thee,   Thou wilt lead me all the way. . . .

289 GIVE OF YOUR BEST TO THE MASTER

H. B. G.

Mrs. Charles Barnard

1. Give of your best to the Mas - ter; Give of the strength of your youth;
2. Give of your best to the Mas - ter; Give Him first place in your heart;
3. Give of your best to the Mas - ter; Naught else is worth-y His love;

REF.—*Give of your best to the Mas - ter; Give of the strength of your youth;*

FINE

Throw your soul's fresh, glowing ar - dor In - to the bat - tle for truth.
Give Him first place in your serv - ice, Con - se-crate ev - 'ry part.
He gave Him-self for your ran - som, Gave up His glo - ry a - bove:

Clad in sal - va-tion's full arm - or, Join in the bat - tle for truth.

Je - sus has set the ex - am - ple; Dauntless was He, young and brave;
Give, and to you shall be giv - en; God His be - lov - ed Son gave;
Laid down His life with-out mur - mur, You from sin's ru-in to save;

rall.   D. C.

Give Him your loy-al de - vo - tion, Give Him the best that you have.....
Grate-ful-ly seeking to serve Him, Give Him the best that you have.....
Give Him your heart's ad-o-ra - tion, Give Him the best that you have.....

LEAD ON, O KING ETERNAL

ERNEST W. SHURTLEFF   LANCASHIRE   HENRY SMART

1. Lead on, O King E - ter - nal, The day of march has come;
2. Lead on, O King E - ter - nal, Till sin's fierce war shall cease,
3. Lead on, O King E - ter - nal, We fol - low, not with fears;

Henceforth in fields of con - quest Thy tents shall be our home.
And ho - li - ness shall whis - per The sweet A - men of peace;
For glad-ness breaks like morn - ing Wher-e'er Thy face ap-pears;

Thro' days of prep - a - ra - tion Thy grace has made us strong,
For not with swords loud clash-ing, Nor roll of stir - ring drums;
Thy cross is lift - ed o'er us; We jour - ney in its light:

And now, O King e - ter - nal, We lift our bat - tle song.
With deeds of love and mer - cy, The heav'n-ly king - dom comes.
The crown a - waits the con - quest; Lead on, O God of might.

J. E. Rankin   W. G. Tomer

1. God be with you till we meet a-gain; By His counsels guide, uphold you,
2. God be with you till we meet a-gain; 'Neath His wings protecting hide you,
3. God be with you till we meet a-gain; When life's perils thick confound you,
4. God be with you till we meet a-gain; Keep love's banner floating o'er you;

With   His sheep se-cure-ly fold you; God be with you till we meet a-gain.
Dai - ly man-na still pro-vide you; God be with you till we meet a-gain.
Put   His arms un-fail-ing round you; God be with you till we meet a-gain.
Smite death's threat'ning wave before you; God be with you till we meet a-gain.

REFRAIN

Till we meet, ... till we meet,   Till we meet at Je - sus' feet;
Till we meet,   till we meet,   till we meet;

Till we meet, ... till we meet,   God be with you till we meet a-gain.
Till we meet,   till we meet,

292 WHEN THE LORD OF LOVE WAS BORN

Hugh Thomson Kerr   Alfred Henry Ackley

1. With shepherds watch-ing lambs and sheep We hear the Christmas song
2. With gold and myrrh and in-cense sweet, With wise men from a- far,
3. O Glo-ria in Ex-cel-sis sing This hap-py Christ-mas morn,

As thru the night they vig-il keep, When the Lord of Love was born.
We come to wor-ship at His feet, Where the Lord of Love was born.
And gold and myrrh and in-cense bring, For the Lord of Love is born.

To Beth-le-hem of fair re-nown We fol-low un-a-fraid,
The stars a-bove are shin-ing bright For all who seek the King,
O come, Lord Je-sus, come and stay, Thou ho-ly Child of God,

For there the peace of God came down When the Lord of Love was born.
And dark-ness is as morn-ing light When the Lord of Love is born.
And may each day be Christ-mas day When the Lord of Love is born.

293 THERE'S A SONG IN THE AIR

Josiah G. Holland

Karl P. Harrington

Adante con moto

1. There's a song in the air! There's a star in the sky! There's a mother's deep
2. There's a tu-mult of joy O'er the won-der-ful birth, For the Virgin's sweet
3. In the light of that star Lie the a-ges impearled; And that song from a-
4. We re-joice in the light, And we ech-o the song That comes down thru the

ritard.   *piu mosso*

prayer, And a ba-by's low cry! And the star rains its fire while the
boy Is the Lord of the earth. Ay! the star rains its fire while the
far Has swept o-ver the world. Ev-'ry hearth is a-flame, and the
night From the heav-en-ly throng. Ay! we shout to the love-ly e-

ritard.

beau-ti-ful sing, For the man-ger of Beth-le-hem cra-dles a King!
beau-ti-ful sing, For the man-ger of Beth-le-hem cra-dles a King!
beau-ti-ful sing In the homes of the na-tions that Je-sus is King!
van-gel they bring, And we greet in His cra-dle our Sav-iour and King!

294 SILENT NIGHT

Joseph Möhr

Franz Gruber

pp

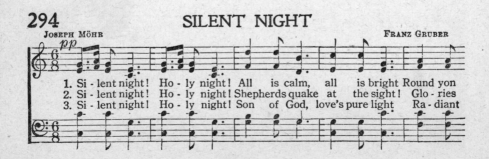

1. Si-lent night! Ho-ly night! All is calm, all is bright Round yon
2. Si-lent night! Ho-ly night! Shepherds quake at the sight! Glo-ries
3. Si-lent night! Ho-ly night! Son of God, love's pure light Ra-diant

SILENT NIGHT

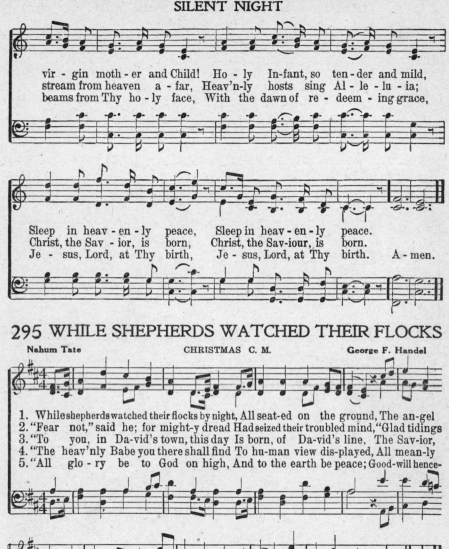

vir - gin moth - er and Child! Ho - ly In - fant, so ten - der and mild,
stream from heaven a - far, Heav'n-ly hosts sing Al - le - lu - ia;
beams from Thy ho - ly face, With the dawn of re - deem - ing grace,

Sleep in heav - en - ly peace, Sleep in heav - en - ly peace.
Christ, the Sav - ior, is born, Christ, the Sav-iour, is born.
Je - sus, Lord, at Thy birth, Je - sus, Lord, at Thy birth. A - men.

295 WHILE SHEPHERDS WATCHED THEIR FLOCKS

Nahum Tate   CHRISTMAS C. M.   George F. Handel

1. While shepherds watched their flocks by night, All seat-ed on the ground, The an-gel
2. "Fear not," said he; for might-y dread Had seized their troubled mind, "Glad tidings
3. "To you, in Da-vid's town, this day Is born, of Da-vid's line, The Sav-ior,
4. "The heav'nly Babe you there shall find To hu-man view dis-played, All mean-ly
5. "All glo - ry be to God on high, And to the earth be peace; Good-will hence-

of the Lord came down, And glory shone a-round, And glo-ry shone a-round.
of great joy I bring, To you and all mankind, To you and all mankind.
who is Christ the Lord; And this shall be the sign, And this shall be the sign:
wrapped in swathing bands, And in a man-ger laid, And in a man-ger laid."
forth from heav'n to men Be-gin, and never cease, Be-gin, and never cease!" AMEN.

296 HARK! THE HERALD ANGELS SING

Charles Wesley

Felix Mendelssohn-Bartholdy

Unison

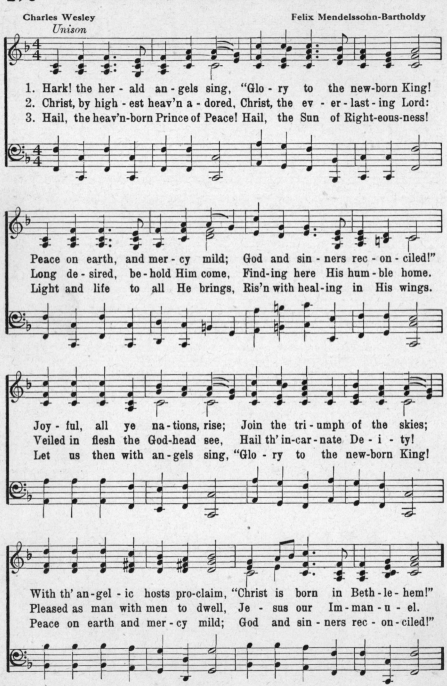

1. Hark! the her - ald an - gels sing, "Glo - ry to the new-born King!
2. Christ, by high - est heav'n a - dored, Christ, the ev - er - last - ing Lord:
3. Hail, the heav'n-born Prince of Peace! Hail, the Sun of Right-eous-ness!

Peace on earth, and mer - cy mild; God and sin - ners rec - on - ciled!"
Long de - sired, be - hold Him come, Find-ing here His hum - ble home.
Light and life to all He brings, Ris'n with heal-ing in His wings.

Joy - ful, all ye na - tions, rise; Join the tri - umph of the skies;
Veiled in flesh the God-head see, Hail th' in-car - nate De - i - ty!
Let us then with an - gels sing, "Glo - ry to the new-born King!

With th' an-gel - ic hosts pro-claim, "Christ is born in Beth - le - hem!"
Pleased as man with men to dwell, Je - sus our Im - man - u - el.
Peace on earth and mer - cy mild; God and sin - ners rec - on - ciled!"

HARK! THE HERALD ANGELS SING

Hark! the her-ald an-gels sing, "Glo-ry to the new-born King!"

297   O COME, ALL YE FAITHFUL

Tr. by Frederick Oakeley   Wade's Cantus Diversi

1. O come, all ye faith-ful, joy-ful and tri-um-phant, O
2. Sing, choirs of an-gels, sing in ex-ul-ta-tion, O
3. Yea, Lord, we greet Thee, born this hap-py morn-ing,

come ye, O come ye to Beth-le-hem; Come and be-hold Him,
sing, all ye bright hosts of heav'n a-bove; Glo-ry to God, all
Je-sus, to Thee be all glo-ry giv'n; Word of the Fa-ther,

REFRAIN

born the King of an-gels.
glo-ry in the high-est. O come, let us a-dore Him, O come, let us a-
now in flesh ap-pear-ing.

dore Him, O come, let us a-dore Him, Christ, the Lord. A-men.

HARK, HARK, MY SOUL!

Frederick W. Faber

Henry Smart

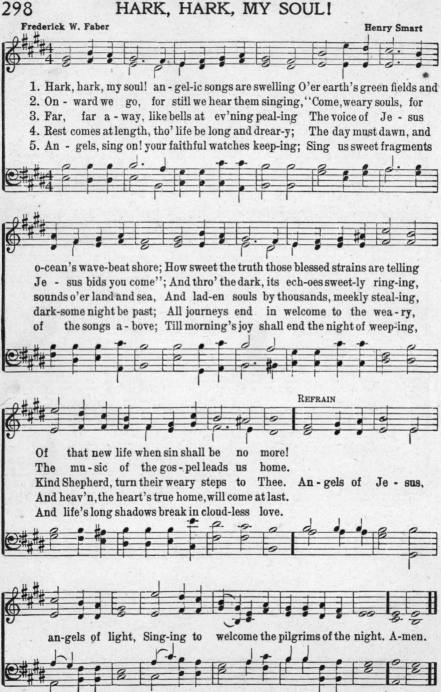

1. Hark, hark, my soul! an - gel-ic songs are swelling O'er earth's green fields and
2. On - ward we go, for still we hear them singing, "Come, weary souls, for
3. Far, far a - way, like bells at ev'ning peal-ing The voice of Je - sus
4. Rest comes at length, tho' life be long and drear-y; The day must dawn, and
5. An - gels, sing on! your faithful watches keep-ing; Sing us sweet fragments

o-cean's wave-beat shore; How sweet the truth those blessed strains are telling
Je - sus bids you come"; And thro' the dark, its ech-oes sweet-ly ring-ing,
sounds o'er land and sea, And lad-en souls by thousands, meekly steal-ing,
dark-some night be past; All journeys end in welcome to the wea-ry,
of the songs a - bove; Till morning's joy shall end the night of weep-ing,

REFRAIN

Of that new life when sin shall be no more!
The mu - sic of the gos - pel leads us home.
Kind Shepherd, turn their weary steps to Thee. An-gels of Je - sus,
And heav'n, the heart's true home, will come at last.
And life's long shadows break in cloud-less love.

an-gels of light, Sing-ing to welcome the pilgrims of the night. A-men.

299 JOY TO THE WORLD!

Isaac Watts

George F. Handel

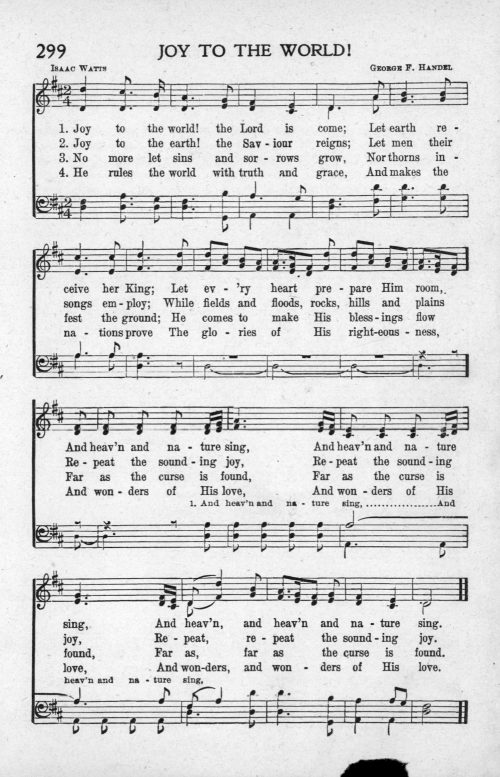

1. Joy to the world! the Lord is come; Let earth re-
2. Joy to the earth! the Sav-iour reigns; Let men their
3. No more let sins and sor-rows grow, Nor thorns in-
4. He rules the world with truth and grace, And makes the

ceive her King; Let ev-'ry heart pre-pare Him room,
songs em-ploy; While fields and floods, rocks, hills and plains
fest the ground; He comes to make His bless-ings flow
na-tions prove The glo-ries of His right-eous-ness,

And heav'n and na-ture sing, And heav'n and na-ture
Re-peat the sound-ing joy, Re-peat the sound-ing
Far as the curse is found, Far as the curse is
And won-ders of His love, And won-ders of His

1. And heav'n and na-ture sing, ... And

sing, And heav'n, and heav'n and na-ture sing.
joy, Re-peat, re-peat the sound-ing joy.
found, Far as, far as the curse is found.
love, And won-ders, and won-ders of His love.

heav'n and na-ture sing,

300 O LITTLE TOWN OF BETHLEHEM

PHILLIPS BROOKS

LEWIS H. REDNER

1. O lit-tle town of Beth-le-hem, How still we see thee lie;
2. For Christ is born of Ma-ry; And gath-ered all a-bove,
3. How si-lent-ly, how si-lent-ly, The won-drous gift is giv'n!
4. O ho-ly Child of Beth-le-hem, De-scend on us, we pray;

A - bove thy deep and dreamless sleep The si-lent stars go by:
While mor-tals sleep, the an-gels keep Their watch of wond'ring love.
So God im-parts to hu-man hearts The bless-ings of His heav'n.
Cast out our sin, and en-ter in, Be born in us to-day.

Yet in thy dark streets shin-eth The ev-er-last-ing Light; The
O morn-ing stars, to-geth-er Pro-claim the ho-ly birth; And
No ear may hear His com-ing, But in this world of sin, Where
We hear the Christ-mas an-gels The great glad ti-dings tell; O

hopes and fears of all the years Are met in thee to-night.
prais-es sing to God the King, And peace to men on earth.
meek souls will re-ceive Him still, The dear Christ en-ters in.
come to us, a-bide with us, Our Lord Em-man-u-el. A-men.

301 CHRIST, THE LORD, IS RISEN TODAY

CHARLES WESLEY   WORGAN   FROM LYRA DAVIDICA

1. Christ the Lord is ris'n to - day, Al - le - lu - ia!
2. Lives a - gain our glo - rious King: Al - le - lu - ia!
3. Love's re - deem - ing work is done, Al - le - lu - ia!
4. Soar we now, where Christ has led, Al - le - lu - ia!

Sons of men and an - gels say: Al - le - lu - ia!
Where, O death, is now thy sting? Al - le - lu - ia!
Fought the fight, the bat - tle won; Al - le - lu - ia!
Fol - l'wing our ex - alt - ed Head; Al - le - lu - ia!

Raise your joys and tri - umphs high, Al - le - lu - ia!
Dy - ing once, He all doth save: Al - le - lu - ia!
Death in vain for - bids Him rise; Al - le - lu - ia!
Made like Him, like Him we rise; Al - le - lu - ia!

Sing, ye heav'ns, and earth re - ply, Al - le - lu - ia!
Where thy vic - to - ry, O grave? Al - le - lu - ia!
Christ has o - pened Par - a - dise. Al - le - lu - ia!
Ours the cross, the grave, the skies. Al - le - lu - ia!

CHRIST AROSE

ROBERT LOWRY   ROBERT LOWRY

1. Low in the grave He lay— Je-sus my Sav-iour! Wait-ing the com-ing day—
2. Vainly they watch His bed— Je-sus my Sav-iour! Vain-ly they seal the dead—
3. Death cannot keep his prey—Je-sus my Sav-iour! He tore the bars a-way—

REFRAIN *Faster*

Je-sus my Lord! Up from the grave He a-rose, With a

He a-rose,

might-y triumph o'er His foes; He a-rose a Vic-tor from the

He a-rose!

dark do-main, And He lives for-ev-er with His saints to reign, He a-

rose! He a-rose! Hal-le-lu-jah! Christ a-rose!

He a-rose! He a-rose!

303 HAIL THE DAY THAT SEES HIM RISE

Charles Wesley   Thomas Clark

1. Hail the day that sees Him rise, Rav-ished from our wish-ful eyes! Christ, a-while to
2. There the pompous tri-umph waits: Lift your heads, e - ter - nal gates; Wide un - fold the
3. Cir-cled round with an - gel pow'rs, Their tri-um-phant Lord and ours, Con-qu'ror o - ver
4. Him tho' high-est heav'n re-ceives, Still He loves the earth He leaves; Tho' re - turn-ing
5. Sav-iour, part-ed from our sight, High a - bove yon az - ure height, Grant our hearts may

mor-tals giv'n, Re - as-cends His na-tive heav'n, Re - as-cends His na - tive heav'n.
ra - diant scene; Take the King of glo - ry in, Take the King of glo - ry in!
death and sin, Take the King of glo - ry in, Take the King of glo - ry in!
to His throne, Still He calls man-kind His own, Still He calls man-kind His own.
thith - er rise, Fol-l'wing Thee be -yond the skies, Fol-l'wing Thee be-yond the skies.

304 THE LORD IS RISEN INDEED

Thomas Kelly   George F. Root

1. The Lord is ris'n in - deed; The grave hath lost its prey;
2. The Lord is ris'n in - deed; He lives, to die no more;
3. The Lord is ris'n in - deed; At - tend - ing an - gels, hear!
4. Then wake your gold - en lyres, And strike each cheer - ful chord;

With Him shall rise the ran-somed seed, To reign in end - less day.
He lives, the sin-ner's cause to plead, Whose curse and shame He bore.
Up to the courts of heav'n, with speed, The joy - ful ti - dings bear:
Join, all ye bright ce - les - tial choirs, To sing our ris - en Lord.

305 MY COUNTRY 'TIS OF THEE

Samuel Francis Smith

Attributed to Henry Carey

1. My coun-try 'tis of thee, Sweet land of lib-er-ty,
2. My na-tive coun-try, thee, Land of the no-ble free,
3. Let mu-sic swell the breeze, And ring thru all the trees
4. Our fa-thers' God, to thee, Au-thor of lib-er-ty,

Of thee I sing; Land where my fa-thers died, Land of the
Thy name I love: I love thy rocks and rills, Thy woods and
Sweet free-dom's song; Let mor-tal tongues a-wake; Let all that
To thee we sing; Long may our land be bright With free-dom's

Pil-grim's pride, From ev-'ry moun-tain side Let free-dom ring.
tem-pled hills; My heart with rap-ture thrills Like that a-bove.
breathe par-take; Let rocks their si-lence break, The sound pro-long.
ho-ly light; Pro-tect us by Thy might, Great God our King.

306 GLORIA PATRI

Charles Meineke

Glo-ry be to the Fa-ther, and to the Son, and to the Ho-ly Ghost; As it

was in the beginning, is now, and ev-er shall be, world without end. Amen, Amen.

307 THE LORD BLESS THEE AND KEEP THEE

(NUM. 6: 24-26)

COPYRIGHT, 1891, BY LUCY RIDER MEYER

Lucy Rider Meyer

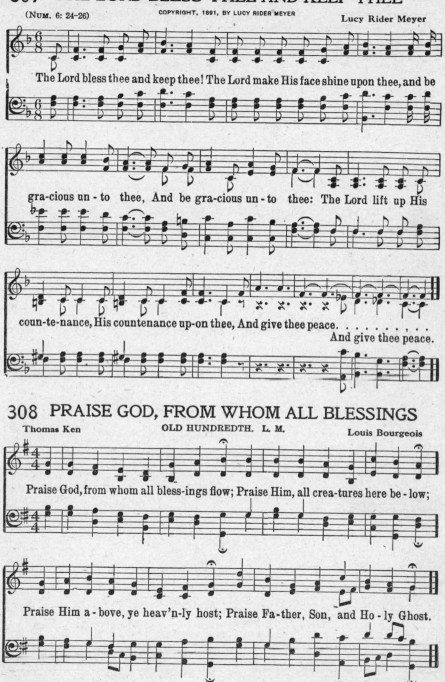

The Lord bless thee and keep thee! The Lord make His face shine upon thee, and be

gra-cious un-to thee, And be gra-cious un-to thee: The Lord lift up His

coun-te-nance, His countenance up-on thee, And give thee peace. . . . .

And give thee peace.

308 PRAISE GOD, FROM WHOM ALL BLESSINGS

Thomas Ken

OLD HUNDREDTH. L. M.

Louis Bourgeois

Praise God, from whom all bless-ings flow; Praise Him, all crea-tures here be-low;

Praise Him a-bove, ye heav'n-ly host; Praise Fa-ther, Son, and Ho-ly Ghost.

309

BLESS THOU THE GIFTS

Samuel Longfellow

Arr. from Robert A. Schumann

Bless Thou the gifts our hands have bro't: Bless Thou the work our hearts have planned;

Ours is the faith, the will, the tho't; The rest, O God, is in Thy hand.

310

ALL THINGS COME OF THEE

Arranged from Beethoven

All things come of Thee, O Lord; and of Thine own have we giv-en Thee. A-MEN.

311

HEAR OUR PRAYER, O LORD

George Whelpton

Hear our prayer, O Lord, Hear our prayer, O Lord; Incline Thine ear to us, And grant us Thy peace. A-MEN.

312

MIZPAH

C. H. G.

Slowly

The Lord watch between me and thee When we are ab-sent one from the other. A-MEN.

Responsive Readings

313 THE KING OF GLORY
Psalms 95:1-6; Psalms 24:3-10

O come let us sing unto the Lord: let us make a joyful noise to the rock of our salvation.

Let us come before his presence with thanksgiving, and make a joyful noise unto him with psalms.

For the Lord is a great God, and a great King above all gods.

In his hand are the deep places of the earth: the strength of the hills is his also.

The sea is his, and he made it; and His hands formed the dry land.

O come, let us worship and bow down: let us kneel before the Lord our Maker.

Who shall ascend into the hill of the Lord? or who shall stand in his holy place?

He that hath clean hands, and a pure heart; who hath not lifted up his soul unto vanity, nor sworn deceitfully.

He shall receive the blessing from the Lord, and righteousness from the God of his salvation.

Lift up your head, O ye gates; and be ye lifted up, ye everlasting doors; and the King of glory shall come in.

Who is this King of glory?

The Lord strong and mighty, the Lord mighty in battle.

Lift up your heads, O ye gates;

Even lift them up, ye everlasting doors; and the King of glory shall come in.

Who is this King of glory?

The Lord of hosts, he is the King of glory.

314 GOD IN NATURE
Psalms 19:1-4; 7-14

The heavens declare the glory of God; and the firmament sheweth his handiwork.

Day unto day uttereth speech, and night unto night sheweth knowledge.

There is no speech nor language, where their voice is not heard.

Their line is gone out through all the earth, and their words to the end of the world. In them hath he set a tabernacle for the sun.

The law of the Lord is perfect, converting the soul: the testimony of the Lord is sure, making wise the simple.

The statutes of the Lord are right, rejoicing the heart: the commandment of the Lord is pure, enlightening the eyes.

The fear of the Lord is clean, enduring forever: the judgments of the Lord are true and righteous altogether.

More to be desired are they than gold, yea, than much fine gold: sweeter also than honey and the honey-comb.

Moreover by them is thy servant warned: and in keeping of them there is great reward.

Who can understand his errors? cleanse thou me from secret faults.

Keep back thy servant also from presumptuous sins; let them not have dominion over me; then shall I be upright, and I shall be innocent from the great transgression.

Let the words of my mouth, and the meditation of my heart, be acceptable in thy sight, O Lord, my strength, and my redeemer.

315 THE WAY AND THE WORD
Psalms 119:1-16

Blessed are the undefiled in the way, who walk in the law of the Lord.

Blessed are they that keep his testimonies, and that seek him with the whole heart.

They also do no iniquity: they walk in his ways.

Thou hast commanded us to keep thy precepts diligently.

O that my ways were directed to keep thy statutes!

Then shall I not be ashamed, when I have respect unto all thy commandments.

I will praise thee with uprightness of heart, when I shall have learned thy righteous judgments.

I will keep thy statutes: O forsake me not utterly.

Wherewithal shall a young man cleanse his way? By taking heed thereto according to thy word.

With my whole heart have I sought thee: O let me not wander from thy commandments.

Thy word have I hid in mine heart, that I might not sin against thee.

Blessed art thou, O Lord: teach me thy statutes.

With my lips have I declared all the judgments of thy mouth.

I have rejoiced in the way of thy testimonies as much as in all riches.

I will meditate in thy precepts, and have respect unto thy ways.

I will delight myself in thy statutes: I will not forget thy word.

316 WISDOM AND UNDERSTANDING
Proverbs 3:13-24, 5-6

Happy is the man that findeth wisdom, and the man that getteth understanding:

For the merchandise of it is better than the merchandise of silver, and the gain thereof than fine gold.

She is more precious than rubies: and all the things thou canst desire are not to be compared unto her.

Length of days is in her right hand; and in her left hand riches and honour.

Her ways are ways of pleasantness, and all her paths are peace.

She is a tree of life to them that lay hold upon her; and happy is every one that retaineth her.

The Lord by wisdom hath founded the earth; by understanding hath he established the heavens.

By his knowledge the depths are broken up, and the clouds drop down the dew.

My son, let not them depart from thine eyes; keep sound wisdom and discretion.

So shall they be life unto thy soul, and grace to thy neck.

Then shalt thou walk in thy way safely, and thy foot shall not stumble.

When thou liest down thou shalt not be afraid; yea, thou shalt lie down, and thy sleep shall be sweet.

Trust in the Lord with all thine heart; and lean not unto thine own understanding.

In all thy ways acknowledge him, and he shall direct thy paths.

317　GOD'S CARE
Psalms 23 and 27

The Lord is my shepherd; I shall not want.

He maketh me to lie down in green pastures.

He leadeth me beside the still waters.

He restoreth my soul:

He leadeth me in the paths of righteousness for his name's sake.

Yea, though I walk through the valley of the shadow of death, I will fear no evil: for thou art with me;

Thy rod and thy staff they comfort me.

Thou preparest a table before me in the presence of mine enemies: thou anointest mine head with oil; my cup runneth over.

Surely goodness and mercy shall follow me all the days of my life; and I will dwell in the house of the Lord forever.

The Lord is my light and my salvation; whom shall I fear?

The Lord is the strength of my life; of whom shall I be afraid?

Though an host should encamp against me, my heart shall not fear:

Though war should rise against me in this will I be confident.

For in the time of trouble he shall hide me in his pavilion:

In the secret of his tabernacle shall he hide me; he shall set me up upon a rock.

And now shall my head be lifted up above mine enemies round about me: therefore will I offer in his tabernacle sacrifices of joy:

I will sing, yea, I will sing praises unto the Lord.

When my father and my mother forsake me, then the Lord will take me up.

318　BEATITUDES
Matthew 5:3-16

Blessed are the poor in spirit:

For theirs is the kingdom of heaven.

Blessed are they that mourn:

For they shall be comforted.

Blessed are the meek:

For they shall inherit the earth.

Blessed are they which do hunger and thirst after righteousness:

For they shall be filled.

Blessed are the merciful:

For they shall obtain mercy.

Blessed are the pure in heart:

For they shall see God.

Blessed are the peacemakers:

For they shall be called the children of God.

Blessed are they which are persecuted for righteousness' sake;

For theirs is the kingdom of heaven.

Blessed are ye, when men shall revile you, and persecute you,

And shall say all manner of evil against you falsely for my sake.

Rejoice, and be exceeding glad: for great is your reward in heaven.

For so persecuted they the prophets which were before you.

Ye are the salt of the earth. Ye are the light of the world.

Let your light so shine before men, that they may see your good works, and glorify your Father which is in heaven.

319 THANKSGIVING AND PRAISE
Isaiah 12

And in that day thou shalt say, O Lord, I will praise thee: though thou wast angry with me, thine anger is turned away, and thou comfortest me.

Behold, God is my salvation; I will trust, and not be afraid: for the Lord Jehovah is my strength and my song; he also is become my salvation.

Therefore with joy shall ye draw water out of the wells of salvation.

And in that day shall ye say, Praise the Lord, call upon his name, declare his doings among the people, make mention that his name is exalted.

Sing unto the Lord; for he hath done excellent things: this is known in all the earth.

Cry out and shout, thou inhabitant of Zion: for great is the Holy One of Israel in the midst of thee.

320 THE LORD IS MY LIGHT
Psalms 27:1-10; 13-14

The Lord is my light and my salvation; whom shall I fear? the Lord is the strength of my life; of whom shall I be afraid?

When the wicked, even mine enemies and my foes, came upon me to eat up my flesh, they stumbled and fell.

Though an host should encamp against me, my heart shall not fear; though war should rise against me, in this will I be confident.

One thing have I desired of the Lord, that will I seek after; that I may dwell in the house of the Lord all the days of my life, to behold the beauty of the Lord, and to inquire in his temple.

For in the time of trouble he shall hide me in his pavilion: in the secret of his tabernacle shall he hide me: he shall set me up upon a rock.

And now shall mine head be lifted up above mine enemies round about me: therefore will I offer in his tabernacle sacrifices of joy; I will sing, yea, I will sing praises unto the Lord.

Hear, O Lord, when I cry with my voice: have mercy also upon me, and answer me.

When thou saidst, Seek ye my face; my heart said unto thee, Thy face, Lord, will I seek.

Hide not thy face far from me; put not thy servant away in anger: thou hast been my help; leave me not, neither forsake me, O God of my salvation.

When my father and my mother forsake me, then the Lord will take me up.

I had fainted, unless I had believed to see the goodness of the Lord in the land of the living.

Wait on the Lord; be of good courage, and he shall strengthen thine heart: wait, I say, on the Lord.

321 THE GREATEST GIFT
I Cor. 13:1-13

Though I speak with the tongues of men and of angels, and have not charity, I am become as sounding brass, or a tinkling cymbal.

And though I have the gift of prophecy, and understand all mysteries, and all knowledge; and though I have all faith, so that I could remove mountains, and have not charity, I am nothing.

And though I bestow all my goods to feed the poor, and though I give my body to be burned, and have not charity, it profiteth me nothing.

Charity suffereth long, and is kind; charity envieth not; charity vaunteth not itself, is not puffed up.

Doth not behave itself unseemly, seeketh not her own, is not easily provoked, thinketh no evil;

Rejoiceth not in iniquity, but rejoiceth in the truth;

Beareth all things, believeth all things, hopeth all things, endureth all things.

Charity never faileth: but whether there be prophecies, they shall fail; whether there be tongues, they shall cease; whether there be knowledge, it shall vanish away.

For we know in part, and we prophesy in part.

But when that which is perfect is come, then that which is in part shall be done away.

When I was a child, I spake as a child, I understood as a child, I thought as a child: but when I became a man, I put away childish things.

For now we see through a glass darkly; but then face to face: now I know in part; but then shall I know even as also I am known.

And now abideth faith, hope, charity, these three; but the greatest of these is charity.

322   FAITH IN GOD
Psalms 37:1-8; 23-26

Fret not thyself because of evil doers, neither be thou envious against the workers of iniquity:

For they shall soon be cut down like the grass, and wither as the green herb.

Trust in the Lord, and do good: so shalt thou dwell in the land, and verily thou shalt be fed.

Delight thyself also in the Lord; and he shall give thee the desires of thine heart.

Commit thy way unto the Lord; trust also in him, and he shall bring it to pass:

And he shall bring forth thy righteousness as the light, and thy judgment as the noonday.

Rest in the Lord, and wait patiently for him: fret not thyself because of him who prospereth in his way, because of the man who bringeth wicked devices to pass.

Cease from anger, and forsake wrath; fret not thyself in any wise to do evil.

The steps of a good man are ordered by the Lord; and he delighteth in his way.

Though he fall, he shall not be utterly cast down; for the Lord upholdeth him with his hand.

I have been young, and now am old; yet have I not seen the righteous forsaken, nor his seed begging bread.

He is ever merciful, and lendeth; and his seed is blessed.

323 THE DAY OF YOUTH
Eccl. 12:1-7; 13-14

Remember now thy Creator in the days of thy youth, while the evil days come not, nor the years draw nigh, when thou shalt say, I have no pleasure in them;

While the sun, or the light, or the moon, or the stars, be not darkened; nor the clouds return after the rain:

In the day when the keepers of the house shall tremble, and the strong men shall bow themselves, and the grinders cease because they are few, and those that look out of the windows be darkened.

And the doors shall be shut in the streets, when the sound of the grinding is low, and he shall rise up at the voice of the bird, and all the daughters of music shall be brought low:

Also when they shall be afraid of that which is high, and fears shall be in the way, and the almond tree shall flourish, and the grasshopper shall be a burden, and desire shall fail; because man goeth to his long home, and the mourners go about the streets:

Or ever the silver cord be loosed, or the golden bowl be broken, or the pitcher be broken at the fountain, or the wheel broken at the cistern.

Then shall the dust return to the earth as it was; and the spirit shall return unto God who gave it. Let us hear the conclusion of the whole matter: Fear God, and keep his commandments: for this is the whole duty of man.

For God shall bring every work into judgment, with every secret thing, whether it be good, or whether it be evil.

324 SUPPLICATION
Psalms 51:1-3; 10-17

Have mercy upon me, O God, according to thy lovingkindness; according unto the multitude of thy tender mercies blot out my transgressions.

Wash me thoroughly from mine iniquity, and cleanse me from my sin.

For I acknowledge my transgressions; and my sin is ever before me.

Create in me a clean heart, O God; and renew a right spirit within me.

Cast me not away from thy presence; and take not thy holy Spirit from me.

Restore unto me the joy of thy salvation; and uphold me with thy free Spirit:

Then will I teach transgressors thy ways; and sinners shall be converted unto thee.

Deliver me from bloodguiltiness, O God, thou God of my salvation; and my tongue shall sing aloud of thy righteousness.

O Lord, open thou my lips; and my mouth shall shew forth thy praise.

For thou desirest not sacrifice, else would I give it: thou delightest not in burnt offering.

The sacrifices of God are a broken spirit: a broken and a contrite heart, O God, thou wilt not despise.

325
THE WORD BECAME FLESH
John 1:1-14

In the beginning was the Word, and the Word was with God, and the Word was God.

The same was in the beginning with God.

All things were made by him; and without him was not any thing made that was made.

In him was life; and the life was the light of men.

And the light shineth in darkness; and the darkness comprehended it not.

There was a man sent from God, whose name was John.

The same came for a witness, to bear witness of the Light, that all men through him might believe.

He was not that Light, but was sent to bear witness of that Light.

That was the true Light, which lighteth every man that cometh into the world.

He was in the world, and the world was made by him, and the world knew him not.

He came unto his own, and his own received him not.

But as many as received him, to them gave he power to become the sons of God, even to them that believe on his name:

Which were born, not of blood, nor of the will of the flesh, nor of the will of man, but of God.

And the Word was made flesh, and dwelt among us, (and we beheld his glory, the glory as of the only begotten of the Father), full of grace and truth.

326
THE WISE AND THE FOOLISH
Matt. 25:1-13

Then shall the kingdom of heaven be likened unto ten virgins, which took their lamps, and went forth to meet the bridegroom.

And five of them were wise, and five were foolish.

They that were foolish took their lamps, and took no oil with them:

But the wise took oil in their vessels with their lamps.

While the bridegroom tarried, they all slumbered and slept.

And at midnight there was a cry made, Behold, the bridegroom cometh; go ye out to meet him.

Then all those virgins arose, and trimmed their lamps.

And the foolish said unto the wise, Give us of your oil; for our lamps are gone out.

But the wise answered, saying, Not so; lest there be not enough for us and you: but go ye rather to them that sell, and buy for yourselves.

And while they went to buy, the bridegroom came; and they that were ready went in with him to the marriage: and the door was shut.

Afterward came also the other virgins, saying, Lord, Lord, open to us.

But he answered and said, Verily I say unto you, I know you not. Watch, therefore, for ye know neither the day nor the hour wherein the Son of man cometh.

327 THE VINE AND THE BRANCHES
John 15:1-14

I am the true vine, and my Father is the husbandman.

Every branch in me that beareth not fruit he taketh away: and every branch that beareth fruit, he purgeth it, that it may bring forth more fruit.

Now ye are clean through the word which I have spoken unto you.

Abide in me, and I in you. As the branch cannot bear fruit of itself, except it abide in the vine; no more can ye, except ye abide in me.

I am the vine, ye are the branches. He that abideth in me, and I in him, the same bringeth forth much fruit: for without me ye can do nothing.

If a man abide not in me, he is cast forth as a branch, and is withered; and men· gather them, and cast them into the fire, and they are burned.

If ye abide in me, and my words abide in you, ye shall ask what ye will, and it shall be done unto you.

Herein is my Father glorified, that ye bear much fruit; so shall ye be my disciples.

As the Father hath loved me, so have I loved you; continue ye in my love.

If ye keep my commandments, ye shall abide in my love; even as I have kept my Father's commandments, and abide in his love.

These things have I spoken unto you, that my joy might remain in you, and that your joy might be full.

This is my commandment, That ye love one another, as I have loved you.

Greater love hath no man than this, that a man lay down his life for his friends.

Ye are my friends, if ye do whatsoever I command you.

328 SEEK YE THE LORD
Isaiah 55:6-13

Seek ye the Lord while he may be found, call ye upon him while he is near.

Let the wicked forsake his way, and the unrighteous man his thoughts: and let him return unto the Lord, and he will have mercy upon him: and to our God, for he will abundantly pardon.

For my thoughts are not your thoughts, neither are your ways my ways, saith the Lord.

For as the heavens are higher than the earth, so are my ways higher than your ways, and my thoughts than your thoughts.

For as the rain cometh down, and the snow, from heaven, and returneth not thither, but watereth the earth, and maketh it bring forth and bud, that it may give seed to the sower, and bread to the eater;

So shall my word be that goeth forth out of my mouth: it shall not return unto me void; but it shall accomplish that which I please, and it shall prosper in the thing whereto I sent it.

For ye shall go out with joy, and be led forth with peace; the mountains and the hills shall break forth before you into singing, and all the trees of the field shall clap their hands.

Instead of the thorn shall come up the fir tree, and instead of the brier shall come up the myrtle tree; and it shall be to the Lord for a name, for an everlasting sign that shall not be cut off.

329 DECISION
Matt. 4:1-11; 17-20

Then was Jesus led up of the spirit into the wilderness to be tempted of the devil.

And when he had fasted forty days and forty nights, he was afterward an hungered.

And when the tempter came to Him, he said, If thou be the Son of God, command that these stones be made bread.

But he answered and said, It is written, man shall not live by bread alone, but by every word that proceedeth out of the mouth of God.

Then the devil taketh him up into the holy city, and setteth him on a pinnacle of the temple,

And saith unto him, If thou be the Son of God, cast thyself down: for it is written, He shall give his angels charge concerning thee: and in their hands they shall bear thee up, lest at any time thou dash thy foot against a stone.

Jesus said unto him, It is written again, Thou shalt not tempt the Lord thy God.

Again, the devil taketh him up into an exceeding high mountain, and sheweth him all the kingdoms of the world, and the glory of them;

And saith unto him, All these things will I give thee, if thou wilt fall down and worship me.

Then saith Jesus unto him, Get thee hence, Satan: For it is written, thou shalt worship the Lord thy God, and him only shalt thou serve.

Then the devil leaveth him, and, behold, angels came and ministered unto him.

From that time Jesus began to preach, and to say, Repent: for the kingdom of heaven is at hand.

And Jesus, walking by the Sea of Galilee, saw two brethren, Simon called Peter, and Andrew his brother, casting a net into the sea; for they were fishers.

And he saith unto them, Follow me, and I will make you fishers of men. And they straightway left their nets, and followed him.

330 GOD'S PRESENCE
Psalms 139:1-10; 23-24

O Lord, thou hast searched me, and known me. Thou knowest my downsitting and mine uprising; thou understandest my thought afar off.

Thou compassest my path and my lying down, and art acquainted with all my ways.

For there is not a word in my tongue, but, lo, O Lord, thou knowest it altogether.

Thou hast beset me behind and before, and laid thine hand upon me.

Such knowledge is too wonderful for me; it is high, I cannot attain unto it.

Whither shall I go from thy spirit? or whither shall I flee from thy presence?

If I ascend up into heaven, thou art there: if I make my bed in hell, behold, thou art there.

If I take the wings of the morning, and dwell in the uttermost parts of the sea;

Even there shall thy hand lead me, and thy right hand shall hold me.

Search me, O God, and know my heart; try me, and know my thoughts; And see if there be any wicked way in me, and lead me in the way everlasting.

331   THE NEW BIRTH
John 3:1-16

There was a man of the Pharisees, named Nicodemus, a ruler of the Jews:

The same came to Jesus by night, and said unto him, Rabbi, we know that thou art a teacher come from God: for no man can do these miracles that thou doest, except God be with him.

Jesus answered and said unto him, Verily, verily, I say unto thee, Except a man be born again, he cannot see the kingdom of God.

Nicodemus saith unto him, How can a man be born when he is old? Can he enter the second time into his mother's womb, and be born?

Jesus answered, Verily, verily, I say unto thee, Except a man be born of water and of the Spirit, he cannot enter into the kingdom of God.

That which is born of the flesh is flesh; and that which is born of the Spirit is spirit.

Marvel not that I said unto thee, Ye must be born again.

The wind bloweth where it listeth, and thou hearest the sound thereof, but canst not tell whence it cometh, and whither it goeth: so is every one that is born of the Spirit.

Nicodemus answered and said unto Him, How can these things be?

Jesus answered and said unto him, Art thou a master of Israel, and knowest not these things?

Verily, verily, I say unto thee, We speak that we do know, and testify that we have seen; and ye receive not our witness.

If I have told you earthly things, and ye believe not, how shall ye believe, if I tell you of heavenly things?

And no man hath ascended up to heaven, but he that came down from heaven, even the Son of man which is in heaven.

And as Moses lifted up the serpent in the wilderness, even so must the Son of man be lifted up:

That whosoever believeth in him should not perish, but have eternal life.

For God so loved the world, that he gave his only begotten Son, that whosoever believeth in him should not perish but have everlasting life.

332   THANKSGIVING AND PRAISE
Psalms 34:1-19, 22

I will bless the Lord at all times his praise shall continually be in my mouth.

My soul shall make her boast in the Lord: the humble shall hear thereof, and be glad.

O magnify the Lord with me, and let us exalt his name together.

I sought the Lord, and he heard me, and delivered me from all my fears.

They looked unto him, and were lightened: and their faces were not ashamed.

This poor man cried, and the Lord heard him, and saved him out of all his troubles.

The angel of the Lord encampeth round about them that fear him, and delivereth them.

O taste and see that the Lord is good: blessed is the man that trusteth in him.

O fear the Lord, ye his saints for there is no want to them that fear him.

The young lions do lack, and suffer hunger: but they that seek the Lord shall not want any good thing.

Come, ye children, hearken unto me: I will teach you the fear of the Lord.

What man is he that desireth life, and loveth many days, that he may see good?

Keep thy tongue from evil, and thy lips from speaking guile.

Depart from evil, and do good; seek peace, and pursue it.

The eyes of the Lord are upon the righteous, and his ears are open unto their cry.

The face of the Lord is against them that do evil, to cut off the remembrance of them from the earth.

The righteous cry, and the Lord heareth, and delivereth them out of all their troubles.

The Lord is nigh unto them that are of a broken heart; and saveth such as be of a contrite spirit.

Many are the afflictions of the righteous: but the Lord delivereth him out of them all.

The Lord redeemeth the soul of his servants: and none of them that trust in him shall be desolate.

333 BROTHERLY KINDNESS
Gal. 6:1-10

Brethren, if a man be overtaken in a fault, ye which are spiritual, restore such an one in the spirit of meekness; considering thyself, lest thou also be tempted.

Bear ye one another's burdens and so fulfil the law of Christ.

For if a man think himself to be something, when he is nothing, he deceiveth himself.

But let every man prove his own work, and then shall he have rejoicing in himself alone, and not in another.

For every man shall bear his own burden.

Let him that is taught in the Word communicate unto him that teacheth in all good things.

Be not deceived; God is not mocked: for whatsoever a man soweth, that shall he also reap.

For he that soweth to his flesh shall of the flesh reap corruption; but he that soweth to the Spirit shall of the Spirit reap life everlasting.

And let us not be weary in well doing: for in due season we shall reap, if we faint not.

As we have therefore opportunity, let us do good unto all men especially unto them who are of the household of faith.

334   PATRIOTIC
Psalm 46:1-4; 7-10

God is our refuge and strength, a very present help in trouble.

Therefore will not we fear, though the earth be removed, and though the mountains be carried into the midst of the sea;

Though the waters thereof roar and be troubled, though the mountains shake with the swelling thereof.

There is a river, the streams whereof shall make glad the city of God, the holy place of the tabernacles of the Most High.

The Lord of hosts is with us; the God of Jacob is our refuge.

Come, behold the works of the Lord, what desolations he hath made in the earth.

He maketh wars to cease unto the end of the earth; he breaketh the bow, and cutteth the spear in sunder: he burneth the chariot in the fire.

Be still, and know that I am God; I will be exalted among the heathen, I will be exalted in the earth.

335 CHRISTIAN LIVING
Romans 12:1-2; 9-17; 20-21

I beseech you therefore, brethren, by the mercies of God, that ye present your bodies a living sacrifice, holy, acceptable unto God, which is your reasonable service.

And be not conformed to this world: but be ye transformed by the renewing of your mind, that ye may prove what is that good, and acceptable, and perfect, will of God.

Let love be without dissimulation. Abhor that which is evil; cleave to that which is good.

Be kindly affectioned one to another with brotherly love; in honour preferring one another;

Not slothful in business; fervent in spirit; serving the Lord;

Rejoicing in hope: patient in tribulation: continuing instant in prayer.

Distributing to the necessity of saints; given to hospitality.

Bless them which persecute you: bless, and curse not.

Rejoice with them that do rejoice, and weep with them that weep.

Be of the same mind one toward another. Mind not high things, but condescend to men of low estate. Be not wise in your own conceits.

Recompense to no man evil for evil. Provide things honest in the sight of all men.

Therefore if thine enemy hunger, feed him; if he thirst, give him drink: for in so doing thou shalt heap coals of fire on his head.

Be not overcome of evil, but overcome evil with good.

336 THE WHOLE ARMOUR
Eph. 6:10-18

Finally, my brethren, be strong in the Lord, and in the power of his might.

Put on the whole armour of God, that ye may be able to stand against the wiles of the devil.

For we wrestle not against flesh and blood, but against principalities, against powers, against the rulers of the darkness of this world, against spiritual wickedness in high places.

Wherefore take unto you the whole armour of God, that ye may be able to withstand in the evil day, and having done all, to stand.

Stand, therefore, having your loins girt about with truth, and having on the breastplate of righteousness;

And your feet shod with the preparation of the gospel of peace;

Above all, taking the shield of faith, wherewith ye shall be able to quench all the fiery darts of the wicked.

And take the helmet of salvation, and the sword of the Spirit, which is the word of God: Praying always with all prayer and supplication in the Spirit, and watching thereunto with all perseverance and supplication for all saints.

337 THE SPIRIT OF WISDOM

Isaiah 11:1-6, 9; Matt. 28:19-20

And there shall come forth a rod out of the stem of Jesse, and a Branch shall grow out of his roots.

And the spirit of the Lord shall rest upon him, the spirit of wisdom and understanding.

The spirit of counsel and might, the spirit of knowledge and of the fear of the Lord;

And shall make him of quick understanding in the fear of the Lord:

And he shall not judge after the sight of his eyes, neither reprove after the hearing of his ears:

But with righteousness shall he judge the poor, and reprove with equity for the meek of the earth:

And he shall smite the earth with the rod of his mouth,

And with the breath of his lips shall he slay the wicked.

And righteousness shall be the girdle of his loins, and faithfulness the girdle of his reins.

The wolf also shall dwell with the lamb, and the leopard shall lie down with the kid;

And the calf and the young lion and the fatling together; and a little child shall lead them.

For the earth shall be full of the knowledge of the Lord.

Go ye therefore, and teach all nations, baptizing them in the name of the Father, and of the Son, and of the Holy Ghost;

Teaching them to observe all things whatsover I have commanded you: and, lo, I am with you always, even unto the end of the world.

338 CHRISTMAS

Luke 2:8-19

And there were in the same country shepherds abiding in the field, keeping watch over their flock by night.

And, lo, the angel of the Lord came upon them, and the glory of the Lord shone round about them: and they were sore afraid.

And the angel said unto them Fear not: for, behold, I bring you good tidings of great joy, which shall be to all people.

For unto you is born this day in the city of David a Saviour, which is Christ the Lord.

And this shall be a sign unto you; Ye shall find the babe wrapped in swaddling clothes, lying in a manger.

And suddenly there was with the angel a multitude of the heavenly host praising God, and saying,

Glory to God in the highest, and on earth peace, good will toward men.

And it came to pass, as the angels were gone away from them into heaven, the shepherds said one to another, Let us now go even unto Bethlehem, and see this thing which is come to pass, which the Lord hath made known unto us.

And they came with haste, and found Mary, and Joseph, and the babe lying in a manger.

And when they had seen it, they made known abroad the saying which was told them concerning this child.

And all they that heard it wondered at those things which were told them by the shepherds.

But Mary kept all these things, and pondered them in her heart

339   GOOD FRIDAY
Isaiah 53:1-7, 10-12

Who hath believed our report? and to whom is the arm of the Lord revealed?

For he shall grow up before him as a tender plant, and as a root out of a dry ground:

He hath no form nor comeliness; and when we shall see him, there is no beauty that we should desire him.

He is despised and rejected of men; A man of sorrows, and acquainted with grief: And we hid as it were our faces from him; he was despised, and we esteemed him not.

Surely he hath borne our griefs, and carried our sorrows: yet we did esteem him stricken, smitten of God and afflicted.

But he was wounded for our transgressions, he was bruised for our iniquities: the chastisement of our peace was upon him; and with his stripes we are healed.

All we like sheep have gone astray; we have turned every one to his own way; and the Lord hath laid on him the iniquity of us all.

He was oppressed, and he was afflicted, yet he opened not his mouth;

He is brought as a lamb to the slaughter, and as a sheep before her shearers is dumb, so he openeth not his mouth.

Yet it pleased the Lord to bruise him; he hath put him to grief:

He shall see of the travail of his soul, and shall be satisfied:

And he was numbered with the transgressors; and he bare the sin of many, and made intercession for the transgressors.

340   PALM SUNDAY
Mark 11:1-10

And when they came nigh to Jerusalem, he sendeth forth two of his disciples. And saith unto them,

Go your way into the village over against you: and as soon as ye be entered into it, ye shall find a colt tied, whereon never man sat; loose him, and bring him.

And if any man say unto you, Why do ye this? say ye that the Lord hath need of him; and straightway he will send him hither.

And they went their way and found the colt tied by the door without, in a place where two ways met: and they loose him.

And certain of them that stood there said unto them, What do ye, loosing the colt?

And they said unto them even as Jesus had commanded: and they let them go.

And they brought the colt to Jesus, and cast their garments on him; and he sat upon him.

And many spread their garments in the way; and others cut down branches off the trees, and strawed them in the way.

And they that went before and they that followed, cried, saying, Hosanna: Blessed is he that cometh in the name of the Lord:

Blessed be the kingdom of our father David, that cometh in the name of the Lord: Hosanna in the highest.

341   EASTER MORNING
Matt. 28:1-10

In the end of the sabbath, as it began to dawn toward the first day of the week, came Mary Magda-le'ne, and the other Mary, to see the sepulchre.

And, behold, there was a great earthquake: for the angel of the Lord descended from heaven, and came and rolled back the stone from the door, and sat upon it.

His countenance was like lightning, and his raiment white as snow:

And for fear of him the keepers did shake, and become as dead men.

And the angel answered and said unto the women, Fear not ye; for I know that ye seek Jesus, which was crucified.

He is not here; for he is risen, as he said. Come, see the place where the Lord lay.

And go quickly, and tell his disciples that he is risen from the dead; and, behold, he goeth before you into Galilee; there shall ye see him: lo, I have told you.

And they departed quickly from the sepulchre, with fear and great joy, and did run to bring his disciples word.

And as they went to tell his disciples, behold, Jesus met them, saying, All hail. And they came and held him by the feet, and worshipped him.

Then said Jesus unto them, Be not afraid: go tell my brethren, that they go into Galilee, and there shall they see me.

342   THE LIVING CHRIST
John 20:6-18

Then cometh Simon Peter following him, and went into the sepulchre, and seeth the linen clothes lie,

And the napkin, that was about his head, not lying with the linen clothes, but wrapped together in a place by itself.

Then went in also that other disciple, which came first to the sepulchre, and he saw, and believed.

For as yet they knew not the scripture, that he must rise again from the dead.

Then the disciples went away again unto their own home.

But Mary stood without at the sepulchre weeping: and as she wept, she stooped down, and looked into the sepulchre,

And seeth two angels in white sitting, the one at the head, and the other at the feet, where the body of Jesus had lain.

And they say unto her, Woman, why weepest thou? She saith unto them, Because they have taken away my Lord, and I know not where they have laid him.

And when she had thus said, she turned herself back, and saw Jesus standing, and knew not that it was Jesus.

Jesus saith unto her, Woman, why weepest thou? Whom seekest thou?

She, supposing him to be the gardener, saith unto him, Sir, if thou have borne him hence, tell me where thou hast laid him, and I will take him away.

Jesus saith unto her, Mary. She turned herself, and saith unto him, Rabboni; which is to say, Master.

Jesus saith unto her, Touch me not; for I am not yet ascended to my Father: but go to my brethren, and say unto them, I ascend unto my Father, and your Father; and to my God and your God.

Mary Magdalene came and told the disciples that she had seen the Lord, and that he had spoken these things unto her.

TOPICAL INDEX

282

GENERAL INDEX

TITLES IN CAPITALS: First Lines in Lower Case

INDEX

CHRISTIAN SERVICE SONGS

CHRISTIAN SERVICE SONGS—1M-200-647